GW00390854

Dear Jo

hope you enjoy first book
have a wonderfull christmas

Alexandar Campion

Learning challenges

With

Dyslexia and Dyspraxia

By Alexandar Campion

CONTENTS

About Me

I have both dyslexia and dyspraxia. I have decided to write this, probably a little too late as there is some great information out there but maybe I have a little bit of a different look on things.

I still have zero idea on grammar and I won't try and fix it! I also don't see it as a disadvantage or a disability. Yes, sometimes annoying and hard work but again these are personal views and outcomes I have experienced and still do to this day.

I will also add in some thoughts that my parents have had over the years and the ups and the downs that are faced or have to be faced.

Introduction

This little book I hope you will find helpful. It isn't a 'how-to' or strict guideline. It also isn't just aimed at the parent to read but the child or person still working though learning issues. It's a different perspective and approach or at the very least, my approach and thoughts on the two lovely labels you're given – that would be a tone of sarcasm… I hate labels!

I hope you have picked up this book and skimmed the first few pages. I want it to be simple but something that I would read or be able to pick up and put down.

So. Where to start? In writing this, I went through a stack of Post-it Notes. My desk was covered and I actually started by designing the book cover. And also yes, by googling how to spell dyslexia and dyspraxia!

Now you may think, why on earth does this person feel he can offer advice on both of the above when he still has to use Google to know how to spell them?

Well, a teacher once told me the best one liner after catching me cheating, e.g. looking in the back of a text book for the correct answers in a test. He said, "Well Alexandar, I guess intelligence isn't always knowing or remembering the answer, but being able to find it." It still ended with a bit of a telling off though. This wasn't in school but in engineering college when I was leaving a ten year career as a chef to go back to school, but I will touch on this later.

Schools are better now but back then, not so much. They are still not perfect by a long shot and you still can face all the same stigma, rubbish and challenges that get tagged on to those lovely labels.

Even as a grown man at 35 years old, I have to work at the challenges I face. But I remember:

(1) If I don't know, I look and if I can't find, I ask.
(2) When becoming a chef, I developed a massive, "F you, I can do it if I keep trying" attitude and not giving in or up. I believe this to be relevant, so I will talk about it later on.

I want to cover things I have found helpful, and also things I have struggled/still struggle with. As I say, this isn't a guide book, text book, self help or autobiography. It's just me talking with you about the random things I have found helpful and some of the things I haven't. Either way, I hope if you're a parent, adult or child, with or learning to live with dyslexia and dyspraxia, this helps.

Chapter 1 (One)

LABELS
Where can we find them?
Well, the dictionary might be an idea!

Dyslexia

*Definition of **dyslexia** – **noun** (from the Oxford Advanced Learner's Dictionary)*

– *a slight disorder of the brain that causes difficulty in reading and spelling, for example, but does not affect intelligence.*

Dyspraxia

*Definition of **dyspraxia** – **noun** (from the Oxford Advanced Learner's Dictionary)*

– *a condition of the brain that develops in childhood causing difficulties with physical movement and writing neatly.*

What these don't tell you is what they really mean.

Dyslexia – A pain in the back side! You will continually have to work to improve on it everyday but it means you will get there. You just have to keep pushing on at it until you find a happy level or to what you need. It does vary from person to person but the work effort doesn't so much.

Dyspraxia – A broad, unhelpful term from the dictionary there!! :(What does this mean? It varies from person to person. But again you can work at most of the issues such as movement, communication, planning and time keeping. These are really key for me. I have become a little what I like to call 'hyper-organised' to combat them. Everything is scheduled. Everything is planned. Even my surprises are set, e.g. the act of being spontaneous which I find hard. So I make a plan to be spontaneous but don't tell anyone and sometimes this is good and works but sometimes the day gets what I call 'scrubbed.'

Movement – again, there are varying degrees of challenges but I love sports and practice makes perfect, eventually.

Clear communication has to be well integrated into both planning and movement. I will address this later.

Why do we like and not like the labels?

The education system and the employment system just LOVE their categories and labels but this is a double-edged sword. It can be useful in access to treatment, help with exams or extra time in both schooling and employment, especially so if you are able to be open and honest about it all.

The reason I say that IF you can be honest with these labels is they can have a stigma attached to them as there are still some misinformed people. While we all have access to information on these labels and what they mean, it doesn't define you or your way of coping with them either.

Remember, though there are many geniuses, successful people, famous people who have these difficulties and access to the worlds resources. It doesn't make that much of a difference – only you can! With hard work, commitment, patience and belief in yourself. The moral of this chapter: To a degree, ignore the labels and the stigma. You are not slow or stupid, thick or dumb. You just need to apply yourself to what you enjoy and you will become by default, the hardest working person out there! I will address how, or how I have found ways to learn new things I didn't ever think I would be able to learn.

In regards to famous or well-known people, the list is:

- Anderson Cooper   Journalist
- Robin Williams   Comedian
- Albert Einstein   Physicist
- Pablo Picasso   Painter/Artist
- Whoopi Goldberg   Comedian, Actress
- Richard Branson   Entrepreneur, Investor, Founder of Virgin Group

- George Washington   First U.S. President
- Octavia Spencer   Actress
- Steve Jobs   The founder of Apple
- Tom Cruise   Actor
- Elon Musk   Entrepreneur & CEO of SpaceX
- Bill Gates   The founder of Microsoft
- Thomas Alva Edison   Entrepreneur / inventor
- Michael Faraday   Entrepreneur / inventor
- Tom Holland   Actor
- Muhammad Ali   Boxer
- Steve Redgrave   Olympic Rower
- Stephen Hawking   Physicist
- Walt Disney   Walt Disney Company
- Steven Spielberg   Film Maker

But really, while some say inspiring, I say become your owninspiration. What do you think? In regards to reading and writing – in school I hated both. I quit French by having my parents write a letter saying basically, "Look at his English. What chance is there of him learning French?" I suggested to my teacher a deal. I would sit at the back of the class and draw, or try to do my homework and not talk to anyone if I wasn't called upon. I never was – odd thing that! Also an odd thing is that my adoptive elder brother is French, from Toulouse. But he is also dyslexic and we understand each other verbally in both languages perfectly. To anyone else this is jibber jabber! ☺

Chapter 2 (Two)

READING! ARGHHHHHHH!!!

Reading... okay. So, both reading and writing and with it our lovely two labels, have a common factor, which is getting your head around the way the letters are put together and how they sound when they are spoken.

Both dyslexia and dyspraxia make this tricky but there are ways and now I even read and write for fun! Things have advanced in reading, I'll give some examples though.

Earlier than middle school I couldn't really read. My parents would try and try. Oddly the alphabet wasn't a problem but the main issue would be skipping lines and then not knowing what or why and then it didn't make any sense.

So how did I learn this? Well in short, I had to go back to basics – the alphabet and then adapt my reading style, e.g. I personally used plain paper not a bookmark to read.

- Bookmarks normally come coloured. I found these to be distracting and again I would jump a line or loose interest.

– Another key point is, interest in what you choose to read, this helps a lot in both aspects.

So A–Z, I now spell using the (NATO) phonetic alphabet. Why? Because I went flying when I was younger and when I used to hear my father's friend, Andrew calling ground control, he would read off the tail number using the (NATO) phonetic alphabet. This way it stuck. Alpha, Bravo, Charlie, Delta... Now this helped and hindered in a way.

It got me interested in the alphabet but verbally and in school it's not how you are taught to pronounce or read the letters. But the NATO phonetic alphabet is what is commonly used when giving your registration plate or post code, for example.

In school it is:

'A' for Apple 'B' for Button 'C' for Camera 'D' for Dice

I will go over this later on in full.

The trick is to slow down the words, giving you the sound of the letter for clearer communication. I will go over this later on also.

So reading teaches spelling. Look up a word like 'Apple', you will know of this more likely from the computer company than the fruit now. But that's okay – you are progressing already.

Movies! This was a brilliant way for me to learn to read. I would love movies and put on the subtitles. I would also do this with the TV sometimes if they had them (this was some time ago).

Now I listen to audiobooks unabridged. This means it's word for word and you can follow along by buying the book as well and any words I don't understand, I underline (annoying my partner) and stick a Post-it Note in the page to look up that word and understand it.

As you can see there are still a lot of words I don't know how to read or spell. Or it's something I like, which is gold dust! Why is this? If you are interested you will want to read it, understand it, go deeper into its meaning, its origin and how you can use this brilliant new word you found in your everyday life or conversation.

NOTE: To Mr Stephen Fry! I loved your books but Christ did I have to look up lots of words! My dictionary hasn't worked that hard in many years!

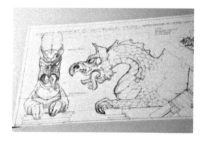

I now read Stephen Fry's books as he read the Harry Potter audio books, word for word. I wasn't that into Harry Potter, although my younger brother was and later my partner. She made me, well, forced me to watch the films and then go to the Harry Potter Studios which is when I actually found I liked it. Why? The design department! It really was incredible.

▲ The five pictures above were taken in the Harry Potter Studios' design department at Warner Brother Studios, London. Three drawings, a model of a whole town and a model of the burrow house, which i just love.

I have always enjoyed design, drawing and architecture (which I later went on to study) and cooking, well cheffing. Three of these things, other than architecture require little reading.

Warning: When reading along with audiobooks and watching movies with subtitles, the written words can sometimes be inaccurate. Also, one I forgot is music videos with subtitles.

NOTE 1: Reading for some dyslexic or dyspraxic people can be very difficult, e.g. the words can jumble on the page. A way I have to look at this is to look at the page as a whole first and then break it down, and view the letters as symbols to indicate a formation of sound in my head or aloud.

NOTE 2: Under pressure, reading is a lot harder especially with exam papers or essays or reports. What I find can happen if rushed or there is distracting noise (not all noise is distracting), it can make it harder. Some noise, e.g. putting on music with no lyrics, I have found to be helpful but it is different for everyone regardless of dyslexia or dyspraxia.

Interest is key. It's the most basic fundamental element in reading and pushing against or breaking through your limitations.

I imagine and hope this is picked up that interest is key. If you are not interested, the end result is that less effort will generally be applied. It is key to remember that basic reading can be so important and if you are reading this or a motorbike manual (I love motorbikes) or a driving theory test, you can do it! Don't allow frustration to set in as this can lead to a sense of failure which is not the case at all. You only fail if you give up!

So, examples. You have this text in front of you and I am guessing you are either a parent wanting to understand and help your child or you're a younger person, and bravo for picking it up and trying! Or, like me, you are older and are wanting to either brush up or want to improve.

Now have you read the above and did you understand it?

Yes ... No ...

Yes = Brilliant

No = Okay, don't panic, do you have a dictionary to hand?

Yes... do you now understand it?

No... Did you highlight the above paragraph and have Google, Siri or Alexa read it to you?

Yes...

No... Okay. Did you ask someone to help you?

Yes?

No... if not look in the back of the book page?

(I will make it even easier ☺)

Assuming you haven't either at this point, thrown the book out the window and cursed my name, but you have tried and understood. That's brilliant. Also if you tried and asked for help, that's okay too! It's also brave, as it is hard but bravo for doing it. It takes great courage to ask for help and it is nothing to be ashamed of and I would be proud as you have problem solved it by yourself by asking.

So, list your goals, read them back to yourself. Now list what you enjoy, ways or things to read or listen to, it's that simple just look up the words you don't (yet) understand. Write/copy the letters/the symbols into the word you want to understand.

NOTE: Keep with you a rubber, pencil, dictionary, thesaurus. If you ever come across a word you don't know, LOOK. IT. UP. Or ask what it means.

One I came across was someone in conversation saying, "He was rather jubilant in the end".

I asked the person first, "What does jubilant mean?" Second, "How do you spell that?" I jotted it down on my phone. This person wasn't hesitant in helping me or concerned with me asking. It's not a word you usually come across in modern day language.

Mini summary of Reading! ARGHHHH!!!

Reading things can be hard; harder if you are not set in the right environment. It takes effort and practice but most of all you must "want, need, enjoy, be interested in" what you are wanting to read and never give up. But remember asking for help isn't giving up. Going into a local library and asking for help also isn't bad. I had to do this many times... what will you pick to read first? Suggestion: SOMETHING FUN!

NOTE for parents – Encouragement

Encouragement is key but constantly offering help is annoying and feels a little like a push. Speaking as someone who struggles with dyslexia and dyspraxia, when I was pushed, I would reject the help offered. But the key to it is, knowing there is help if needed or wanted. It will be in some ways, your learning difficulty as much as theirs – not so much as in 'difficulty' or 'disability' but let's replace that with learning challenges. That is how I view them; as challenges, goals to be scored, different approaches to be taken. Be patient and prepared to allow some mistakes to happen... it will be tricky. My parent's approaches were neither wrong or right but were different.

My Father would see I loved to take things apart and put them back together again. He saw if I could see, I could do. One Christmas he bought me a Haynes manual for our old Land Rover. He would take out a part whilst reading the book aloud and showed me it. He then pointed to the page. He would say, "This is a carburettor. See, it says..." And I learned how to read and spell this way. Also fix other parts and ask questions. It was fun and interesting for me.

My mother – The Lioness. She constantly had to fight with the schools and the teachers to get me the help I needed. It was a little different back then, however she never let that annoyance transfer onto me. It was always support and kindness. Not pity. Sometimes if she could see I was struggling, it was a kick up the backside. If I was putting it to one side or giving up or she would try to tell me a different way, explaining why it would be more helpful.

Now as I said I hate labels and the term difficulties and disability in regards to learning. I should expand on it.

Dyslexia and dyspraxia is not slightly going to make things harder. It will most certainly make things harder. Now, difficulty is negative not impossible but sounds awful to hear. Disability is even worse paralysed, incapacitated this is NOT what it is at all. My view is that it is a challenge and would go as far as to say learning challenges. As there will be both positives and just slower learning times but with this comes a much more well-rounded knowledge base and a better sense of achievement and focus can be obtained. You just have to be willing to try different ways, methods, trials, tests and be willing to never give up on the challenge.

NOTE: Interesting side note – accepting you or your child has a learning difficulty (challenge) is going to be hard but!... By accepting it, it can be overcome. Things to look out for in yourself or your child is the frustration, anger, annoyance, self doubt, anxiety and depression it can cause.

However, now you are aware of these emotions, like the labels, you acknowledge them, yes. Yield to them, no. There is no path which this will be of benefit to anyone. Focus on the basics – the rest is just going to be a little more challenging but if you pick enjoyable subject fields, even more complex ones, it will come to you and you will naturally work harder than your peers but have a better understanding in the end.

- Lastly, I will discuss emotional states later on and how I have seen, felt and overcome them with the right people and methods around me! ☺

Chapter 3 (Three)

LEARNING LETTERS

Alphabet, symbols, shapes bringing together to form Words

Right, I was going to jump straight into writing but before I do that I think it's time for a bit of basics which will be the alphabet. First my view on it – shapes of letters and then forming them into words.

Firstly, a point of view. When I see letters, I see shapes or what I call symbols, I say symbols as when they are pronounced they make a sound and when put together they form a word... (sound I will later address under verbal communication!)

Now, the alphabet is scary but it is 26 (twenty six) letters long. All have a different sound, but if we think of the ancient Egyptians who would write using hieroglyphs where the symbols, shapes, pictures were used to clearly communicate information or a story or warning. It was over 700 (seven hundred) symbols long. Now 4000 (four thousand) years laters you need only deal with 26 (twenty six) letters or symbols! (So not too bad and a little less scary!)

A – this is upper case, known as a capital letter. In the word 'apple' the very first part is pronounced or spoken as "AH".

Now when I am writing something quick, I use all capital letters, no joined up handwriting. But I will go on to explain this in the next chapter and give reasons why.

Here is the alphabet with capitals and then lowercase, which look like this:

a = lower case "A"

*The alphabet:

A a – Apple   B b – Bear   C c – Cow   D d – Dice

E e – Elephant   F f – Fox   G g – Giraffe   H h – Hat

I i – Ice   J j – Jam   K k – Koala   L l – Lion

M m – Monkey   N n – Nest   O o – Owl   P p – Penguin

Q q – Queen   R r – Rainbow   S s – Spider   T t – Tiger

U u – Umbrella   V v – Violin   W w – Wolf

X x – X-ray   Y y – Yak   Z z – Zebra

The underlined letters are the capital or "upper case" letters and the ones next to them are the same letter but lower case letters.

Below here are examples of upper and lower case working together:

My name is Mr Alexandar Campion.

I have understood this part so far, however it is still tricky.

Yours Faithfully

To Mr/Miss/Mrs/Ms/Dr/Sir or Madam (reader of this book), Why we have upper and lower case letters, I will explain in writing. Firstly though, have a go at writing them now.

Before you start, use a pencil and have a rubber to hand or if you have some tracing paper, all you have to do to improve your letters in a way is to copy or even trace over them. This will help you with the form of our shapes, letters, 'symbols'!

Note – To stop worrying about letters, I focus more on their shape and form – this is why I look at them as symbols and this is like drawing! Now this is actually called calligraphy which is different types of fonts you would find on your computer. But for the basics let's practice these.*

Now this is the basic way of making your symbols (letters) legible to the reader. "Legible" means able to read what you have written. Personally, handwriting is hard. Have you ever noticed a doctor's note and handwriting? They usually have awful handwriting. My younger brother who can fluently speak 2 (two) other languages and holds a degree in French has what you would call "illegible" handwriting, meaning you can't read it!

These are the basic building blocks. Practice them and find your favourite way of drawing these letters so anyone could read or at the very least, be able to read it.

These are the basic building blocks. Practice them and find your favourite way of drawing these letters so anyone could read or at the very least, be able to read it.

Try these below...

My name is ....

I like to write ....

My favourite colour is ....

I will keep trying till I am happy.

Next is writing. You're on a roll. WELL DONE ☺

Chapter 4 (Four)

OK, HANDWRITING, SPELLING, GRAMMAR. EEEEEKKKKKKKKK!

How necessary is it to you?

First, I will cover writing. When in school, pen to paper, e.g. handwriting and what I can only describe to you as a mental block towards it, was so daunting! The idea of making the pen form the letters in the correct way was scary, hard and I never thought of looking at them as shapes until later in life, hence switching these chapters around.

Now writing, for me I prefer pen to paper. Strange. Well yes and no. I will explain. I got put on a computer at school. However, this while making my writing (typing) legible, didn't really help with the spelling. But it was a good short term stop gap.

The difference now is you can just speak to Siri, Alexa, Google or even Dragon Dictate (which in university they made me use their trial program 🐲) for writing terms these are helpful in the sense of spelling and I would say they catch 80% of the words spoken and spell them correctly.

Note – The slight catch; they won't get every word. Okay, not too bad but they will not put in the full stops, commas or understand grammar, but they are still advancing even as I write this in now in 2021.

As I say, they are a good tool for your tool box in writing, like audiobooks are in reading along with them.

Writing – I love pen to paper but I have 3-4 styles of writing and still, what I would say, is a work in progress on being grammatically correct. Here is the thing I have found. I can happily get my point, view or opinion across in a written format via letter, text, email or this book. (Fingers crossed ☺)

Moral of this is being where you want to be and be willing to work at it until you are happy. Mistakes will happen of course but most get over looked and if you are concerned about it, have it checked over, or what I do is read it aloud to myself. You will start to notice the missing words. Also if the form of your letters doesn't seem right it is usually a mistake, but you then have just spotted it and corrected it! (I certainly know I read this back and had to fix a lot of mistakes... still learning)

I will start with handwriting, known as either font style handwriting or even calligraphy.

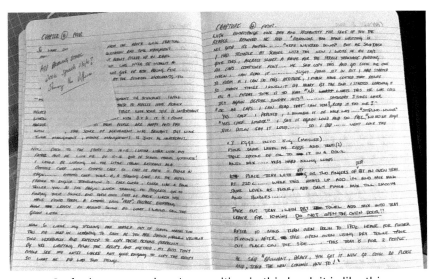

So for instance, when I am writing in this book it is like this

This is all capitals, clear spacing so it allows me to correct and spot mistakes. Also note: all caps is like a computer keyboard or phone letters – all uppercase!

Apple keyboard

It starts all caps. Until you add a full stop

Dell keyboard

Notes on iPhone does switch to lower case after the first letter.

The fourth (4th) style is just a bit of a mash up of all three combined. It is more like a code. I can read it but it is a mess. Most importantly I can read it and only use it for me (not the best for practice).

But let's address the styles or the fonts.

(1) As I have said, it is clear, slow, all caps well spaced. It is actually what I used to 'pen out' this book. Well, first it was mostly on Post-it Notes and backs of envelopes and scrap paper.

(2) Say an idea has hit me, I want it down on paper as quickly as possible. It's just quick, I get it. I think my teachers would still frown at this but what does that matter now? Nothing and its notes for me and I'm ok with it.

> SAY AN idea has hit me, I want it down
> on paper. its quick, I get it, I think my teachers
> would still frown at this but what does that matter
> now ... Nothing & its ndes for me and im ok
> & that.

(3) Okay, scrolled writing like this isn't used much but if I am say, leaving a thank you note or letter to family, I will write this way. Why? I enjoy the challenge and love the look, also it is nice for invitations too.

> Okay Scrolled writing like this isnt
> used much but if I am, say, leaving a
> thankyou note ok letter to family I will
> write this way. why? well I enjoy the
> challenge and love the look, also nice for
> invitations too.

What do all of these fonts, styles have in common? I am happy with all three, what is the difference? Apart from the style, it would be the context of the situation in which I'm writing and which is either easier or appropriate for the deemed recipient.

Example/Explained

1 – Would be a note to a boss or peer, quick and short, but needing to get my point across. Handwritten – this is rare now but can work in school if you are struggling with joined up writing as it will be more legible or readable.

3 – Is more of an upscale version of what schools would want however, it's time consuming and takes practice. Nice as I say for the odd letter, note to a friend or partner or a party invite.

The fourth is a combination of capitals and scroll. Again I use this more for my own personal writing or notes.

With all of these though I can read and determine what is necessary for the situation in hand. Try some styles, copy, feel what is comfortable for your hand and feels smooth and legible. Basically practice. Enjoy? Legible? = Go. If not, try a different one or design your own?

NOTE – To parents/reader or user of this book.

With dyslexia and dyspraxia, to simplify this part of the chapter, I will cover this in the verbal communication chapter. But writing is very similar to speech you change the tone and pitch of your voice to suit the situation. No?

For instance, if I am talking to friends or mates in person, or when I am out or on the phone, it is more relaxed. Slang and abbreviations I would have learnt or grown up with come into play.

Now, if I am speaking in public to people or a bank manager, it changes. I slow down, think of the words I am going to say and how I will pronounce them.

- Listen to people talking to different demographics (types of people). This will help you understand, especially family talking to family or friends compared to how they speak to their doctor or bank manger or a businesses person or like me, a customer.

- Funny side note: My mother does this a lot. If she is talking to friends from home, ha :) very different to how she would talk to a doctor or bank manager. I do the same! It's funny when you catch yourself doing it but a lot can be learnt.

Which again is context and the place and situation you are in but the main thing is <u>YOU</u> are comfortable and when writing, it is legible.

Sorry if that part dragged on a bit but it is a key factor and something with dyslexia and dyspraxia I struggled with a lot. However, the next part might be a little more fun!!

Spelling – putting our lovely "symbols" (letters) together to make words.

By default/design you should now be able to spell...

Apple, bear, cow, dice, elephant, fox, giraffe, hat, ice, jam, koala, lion, monkey, nest, owl, penguin, queen, rainbow, spider, tiger, umbrella, violin, wolf, x-ray, yak, zebra.

Above is the A-Z of the alphabet. Also if you notice, I have been a little sneaky and put page numbers and the spelling at the bottom of each page, also at the top of the chapters of this book.

NOTE – If like me you may have listened to this book and come across a word you don't understand, you can underline it, hear how it is spoken. Now write it down and either look it up on your phone or computer by copying the letters or grabbing your dictionary/thesaurus and see its meaning that way. Even more cheekily, I have picked some words out and put them in the back of the book which of course, I will read to you.

Remember – Speed in spelling doesn't help but knowing where to find the answer is intelligence. So, do any of the above and you will hopefully have some of the basics covered! Found and learnt them yourself. Well done! Even when writing this, as you will remember I still learnt new words which I am "jubilant" about. Yes... laugh out loud (lol) ☺

Let's not stop there on spelling. The assortment of our letters into words are always changing and evolving or adapting like us. As humans for instance, the reason why our front teeth over hang our lower is due to the use of cutlery! An adaption we have made to ourselves without knowing.

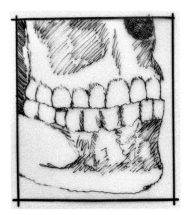 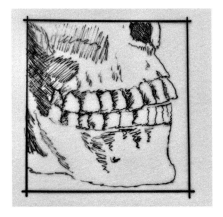

NOTE – Human jaw before cutlery on left. On right after showing over hang of the top of the jaw. This is because we needed to use less of our teeth to chew and the introduction of processed foods.

Spelling is somewhat like handwriting - you will have some things you enjoy and many you probably won't. Being dyslexic and dyspraxic can be daunting. Scary to hear however, it can allow you to focus on things you enjoy.

That is the cheat or simplest part to the whole big picture. For some dyslexic and dyspraxic people they find it's numbers they enjoy. For others it's art, drawing, photography, cooking, woodwork. Shapes and colours can be easier for some of us more then others. Add in with each of these activities there are new words that are interesting to learn and you can expand your spelling and vocabulary by just finding your most enjoyable subject field, then looking up the words that link into it.

My little story is as follows:

It's around 2001, year 11 in school. I had as I say, given up on school by this point. I could just about read but the exams came up. Long story short - I got 1 GCSE pass grade in design technology. A year before this however, I had started work at a small Italian restaurant. As soon as the bell would ring, I was out the door. Also sometimes my dad would let me skip a day off school to work doing landscaping, turfing, decking, fencing, lawn mowing, etc.

NOTE – Don't skip school! This was the wrong way, but I was lucky and a hard worker, so I did what I enjoyed. Dad rightly saw I would have probably started to skip school and instead of letting me just do that and do nothing, he said, "You will work with me." The job I got at the Italian restaurant, I got because I loved Italian food and the lady whose son owned the restaurant told him to hire me as I was always asking questions about the food!

With my father, I learnt more maths than I ever did in school. For example, what I would still call practical maths - feet to meters, how to calculate an abnormal shape, depth and weight and levels. Also I learnt the reward of a hard days work or weekend. Dad would pay me a fair wage and I learnt how to write a quote, e.g. going to the builders merchants, copying the words adding the quantity required… say 20 ton bags of hardcore type 1 with 3 rolls of 3m x 20m underlay for delivery to X address. This was on the quote sheet for the job which was to gravel a driveway.

What did I learn from the above? Well, practical maths, spelling, forming a quotation and time management. All of these I personally hadn't really picked up in school. The other big lesson I learnt was to never be without a job and work hard and not give up. Also asking for help wasn't a bad thing, from the builders merchants to my father.

NOTE – Planning & time management or schedules. I will write a chapter about these aspects later on as they have really helped me later in life. Being strict with yourself is important when it comes to time management with dyslexia and dyspraxia. It is I've found, to be harder however, to stick to plans, times and schedules. People are happy and pay if you do! Wow, getting paid! Sense of achievement was brilliant but like time management, money management is just as important.

Back to the story...

So at 14–15 years old, I would work with my father and he with me learning these practical skills. By 15–16 it was the end of school thank goodness. It couldn't come soon enough for me!! I had been working in the little Italian restaurant as a commis chef to become chef de partie (French in origin). As commis chef, you are a trainee chef or the actual French to English translation is chef clerk – clerk like a bank teller. You do the basic work training to progress on to finding your skills, then on to a chef de partie when you have found them. A commis chef will 'prep' or prepare everything, learn all round skills and do what I would call the grunt work.

Now while my spelling had improved out of school, maths too, this did help in learning to cook as you are shown visually and told verbally and expected to copy these actions perfectly. But yes, writing down the recipe and the method, my boss Tony could see my notes where not good enough to copy the exact recipe. So what he did was two things.

With annoyance one day, and a lot of profanity (removed for the sake of the reader), he said, "Alexandar, your handwriting is not good. It's awful." (Very watered down version). But he carried on, "I also had trouble at school with this. Now I write in all caps." Across the table he slid a sheet of paper with a recipe for the perfect Yorkshire pudding. All caps computer typed. He said, "Copy this and go cook me one when I can read it." Slight panic set in but I had started to form an 'I can do this attitude'. I must have copied that recipe so many times, I knew it by heart by the end, I started on the Friday and took it to him. "No! What's this?" He was cross. "Try again before Sunday hits." Saturday and 3 times later, "Okay... All caps... I can read that. Can you? Read it to me." I replied, "Yes, chef." I sped mumbled it. Halfway he cut me off, slamming his palm on the table. "Stop! No, no, no. Louder. Slow down and say it loud." So I did. Loud and too fast. Another slam on the table! "No, no, no, no. Right, SLOW down, say it loud." So I did.

It went like this:

3 EGGS INTO JUG AND MEASURE
FLOUR SAME LEVEL AS EGGS
ADD 2 TABLESPOONS OF OIL TO IT AND MIX
UNTIL SMOOTH AND MIX HARD SO NO LUMPS.

GET DEEP TRAY WITH 50g OR 2 FINGERS OF BEEF FAT IN THE OVEN AT 220 DEGREES CENTIGRADE.

WHILE THIS HEATS UP,
ADD MILK TO YOUR MIX - SAME LEVEL AS THE FLOUR,
ADD A PINCH OF SALT AND MIX IN SLOWLY
UNTIL BUBBLES FORM ON TOP
TAKE OUT THE TRAY, WITH <u>DRY</u> TOWEL AND ADD THE
MIX INTO THE TRAY AND PLACE INTO THE OVEN

LEAVE FOR 10 MINS <u>DO NOT OPEN THE OVEN DOOR</u>

AFTER THE 10 MINS TURN DOWN TO 170c LEAVE FOR
FURTHER 15 MINS, AFTER THIS OPEN OVEN USING DRY
TOWEL TAKE OUT PLACE ON SIDE...
THIS WILL BE FOR TWO PEOPLE.

He said, "Brilliant... Bravo, you got it! Now go cook 20 please and oh, please teach the new commis how to!"

What Tony did there (which at the time I thought he was just being – well, I'll let you think of the word!) was not "monkey see, monkey do" but to build up my confidence. By not taking any backchat or excuses he only wanted consistent, clear translation of information to get the job done.

So, now I am in an Italian restaurant. It is worth pointing out Sunday roast with Yorkshire pudding is not Italian! It did make him A LOT of money on Sundays – they are the easiest days. Roast dinners mainly, some odd other dishes but rarely.

This taught me another lesson: knowing your market, e.g. your customers wants and needs which in catering/cheffing, is a big part of it. The other part of this is that it all has to be done within 15 minutes of them placing an order or they will complain and then Tony would throw a pan at the wall or would scream at you!

Lastly, learning timing is another key lesson. Planning is key. If you get both right - no angry Tony but a happy Tony and a share of the tips!!

NOTE – I think Cheffing was a hard way to build confidence but I also believe Tony, the restaurant owner was dyslexic and dyspraxic himself. So he knew how to push me. Later on, when I looked through Tony's recipe book that contained all the things I had been cooking, it was all capitals and drawings of the dish – PLANNING! Labeled components teaching me the words, e.g. the spelling. So here in this example, it was a different case of monkey see, monkey do... copying the recipes, learning the spelling and detailed planning of dishes and timing. Consistency was key in cheffing.

Also just to add in a high stress environment like cheffing, they want you to be direct, "Yes chef. No chef. How many chef? I don't know chef, I'm sorry chef or I got this wrong chef." The point is if you're direct and honest about problems (not just as a chef), people respect it.

As I said, I think Tony was dyslexic and dyspraxic himself – it is a suspicion. I suspect he was. He used to sometimes jump out the back window to avoid investors in the return of a vender looking for the bill to be paid. Managing money is something I also struggled with but I will touch on this later.

NOTE – To parents/reader. A small side to this – with dyslexia and dyspraxia is time management and judging a social situations can take a while to understand. Back in 2001–2002, there were less rules and it could be overlooked or put aside, a bit like minimum wage guidelines. For instance, for me, my mother looking out for me as Tony did take some advantages. On a Sunday evening after a shift he would have me folding leaflets until 2am from a 9am start.

This happened a couple of times with Tony saying it was part of the learning process. Also that he would be busier so we would be paid more (NOT THE CASE). I was just 15/16 at the time and still in school. My phone rang. It was my mother calling at 1am. "Where are you?!" She was angry. I had school the next day. I said, "Erm, I'm folding some leaflets for the restaurant. Tony needs more business and I'll get more money!" (I had become obsessed.) Silence... "Mum? Er mum? Still there? Can you hear me?" Pause... "Yes." She said, "Well, it's 1am and I hope you'll be a f***king millionaire one day! Get. Home. Now." Hangs up... oh. "Tony I have to go home. My mum is angry as anything." Tony's reply, "Ah okay." Maybe he realised the time or that he just enraged my mother, the Lioness. Basically taking the mick. "You get home. See you Friday," he said.

Ironically, my mum looking out for me like this was the right thing. At the same time, in that moment I didn't get the problem. I liked working. She explained at my age it wasn't acceptable and when she reads this, yes she was right, which will undoubtably make her smile! Thank you, mother!

What stuck with me the most from that night was my mother saying, "Well, I hope you'll be a f***king millionaire!" Hmm I like the sound of that! Hard work = money = saved = more money, then how to make more? Now thanks to mum, I am! Through late nights and hard work. But she was right, I wasn't getting paid after 9pm so I was doing 4 hours of work for free!

By this point I was a chef de Partie. I had picked up some French, a lot of Italian swear words and also how to say some basics, e.g. hello, good evening, 1–10 etc.

As I say, my time with Tony came to an end. My mum, knowing I had now found a skill I enjoyed and could read and spell recipes and understand their context, showed me how to put together a CV (curriculum vitae). It was just an A4 page with a written reference from Tony that my mother helped me get. It landed me with a good job in a restaurant out of the way, a couple of villages across. I had good (well better) communication skills at this point (which I will cover later), better legible writing/spelling and able to verbally communicate in my interviews which I practiced. Interviews I will cover later in verbal communication.

But like mistakes – hands up, be honest and ask how you went wrong. I have never walked out of an interview without either learning something new or the job itself.

– Moral of the story and how this relates to spelling:
If you look at my story, I have started to use longer words to share a little bit of my learning and progress with spelling. Also reading helps spelling. So, what words have you picked out, noticed or not recognised or understood? Are you wanting to learn them? If so, underline them. This is a process that won't come all at once and you will pick up parts of what you enjoy or have enjoyed.

NOTE – Within this chapter you should now have the words to write a CV. If you don't feel confident, in the back of the book there is a template you can fill out using your new words.

NOTE – To parents. I and many other dyslexic and dyspraxic people will do things that need to be looked out for, and it is a tricky one to navigate as you see progress.

(1) I obsess over things and commit fully into them. I also will not understand all of the social settings or struggle to balance the work/home life. I will go more in-depth into this later in the emotions chapter.

(2) Work to me now is an escape. I am fully engaged with a project. I find myself really content and happy, even when under pressure or stress. This isn't the same for everyone, however finding a subject field you enjoy and keeping busy is good. Lack of this, can lead to laziness. It can easily set in and take hold which leads to other problems. So it is a balancing act. Hopefully by context you can understand but I will go further into emotional states, timing and management in later chapters.

(If you the reader, have read this, sometimes the extra set of eyes on you is a good thing as you won't always be able to quickly adapt to different situations but you will learn this more and more over time.)

WOW. We are coming a long way in chapter four. So the other and last part of this chapter is about grammar!!

This to me is still really hard. Now the question is a simple one... How necessary is grammar to my everyday life?

- To me, I have found some ways of short cutting grammar. Also in university when writing a complaint to the Head of Architecture's Secretary, the head replied how poorly written my email was. That made me really annoyed with myself. So I corrected my own mistakes, highlighted the issues and sent in a further complaint about his reply with him knowing about me being dyslexic and dyspraxic to the Head of the University. This time taking my time.

Taking a few knocks is going to happen. Don't get angry with yourself or others and react. It increases speed and chances of mistakes sky rocket! You will have to come to your own understanding of this and your trigger points. It's important to keep them in check and educate... don't shout or scream. Just describe your feelings.

Okay so, grammar

I need a coffee break before writing this to think of the best and hopefully, the easiest way to describe it and explain it. .... (Long pause!)

Grammar with dyslexia and dyspraxia is again different for each person. However, there are some common mistakes you can avoid.

Words form sentences to form paragraphs. Now, grammar allows your sentences to flow into a paragraph of writing and make sense to the reader, giving a sense of context, e.g. the way in which it is read and then understood emotionally.

Identifying your reader or recipient of your text, email or letter is key to the level of grammar required.

Also is what the literary (written) context of what you are trying to say. For instance, I will tell you some things wrongly and then correctly. See if you are reading it to yourself or listening to it, if you can tell the difference.

(1) I play chess good. = I play chess well. (adverbs)
(2) My car beautiful, after washed it. = My car is beautiful after I washed it. (The verb 'be')
(3) Last night I cry at this book. = Last night I cried at this book. (Past tense) – Note: I hope you didn't!!
(4) What time it is? = What time is it? (Word order) Note – Yoda from Star Wars could have learnt from this!!

Out of these 4, did you hear or see the difference? Hopefully you got a couple or all. If not, no worries try again!

By understanding the contexts and the differences is how your sentences will flow more easily.

The next most common mistake and one that I find I still make at 35 years of age with dyslexia and dyspraxia, is a simple one. I write how I speak in my head! Now, when it comes to pen and paper I still struggle by doing two key things wrong.

(1) I will try to string together 2-3 sentences into a paragraph and not add any grammar or full stops, making it hard for people to understand. What's missing is called punctuation which are these commonly used symbols. , . ! ? " " ... & ( ) /

(2) I will write what I hear in my head or the way in which I talk. Sometimes missing a word or not writing in the correct tense, e.g. future, present, past.

I hope to finish this book soon! - A wish.
I will finish this book soon! - A goal/statement.
I have finished this book soon! - See the mistake?
I have to finish this book soon! - Corrected.

Another good example would be say, a weather reporter. I will read as written...

Today in Dorset there will be some good weather there will be some showers across the west part of it later on but we must still wear sunblock as it will be sunny and reaching temperatures of 34c in parts thats it for today see you tomorrow

Today in Dorset, there will be some good weather. There will be some showers across the west part of it later on but we must still wear sunblock as it will be sunny and reaching temperatures of 34c in parts. That's it for today! See you tomorrow!

There are some more brief examples of grammar, written and spoken in a chapter later on where I will address this and verbal communication.

For now, sentences of paragraphs or the slight cheat...

If I'm writing an email or a letter, I will consider it's context (what I want it to say). Also who it is for and the easiest way for me to be able to write it in grammatically correct English so that the person reading it will be able to understand.

To you the reader – If you are a parent, child, or you are just wanting to improve your writing and reading skills, I hope you are finding this book useful.

The aims were to:

- Simply put into context a book where you would learn by reading or listening.
- To improve your spelling by slowly introducing newer and longer words.

– For it to be able to help you understand some of the difficulties or what I call 'challenges', facing you or your child with dyslexia and dyspraxia.

That is how I tend to break a paragraph down – with bullet points! To the point, clear and concise to both of us, hopefully?

NOTE – Nouns, pronouns, verbs, adverbs, adjectives, articles, prepositions, conjunctions and interjection. All parts of grammar. Also you have punctuation, signs and symbols. If you go to the back of this book (page 151) you will see charts on what all of the things above mean.

Summary of chapter 4

The only one question you have to ask yourself is, where are you comfortable? As I say, in the back of this book, there's not only charts on all of the above, but useful draft letters, and a couple of other bits and bobs to get you comfortable and happy in your own writing.

CHAPTER 5 (Five)

ADDRESSING SCHOOL

I need to address a subject... My schooling and school. In 2021, I am 35 years of age and with the benefit on hindsight, it was not good, but it was not awful. The part you have to remember is that this was some time ago and things have got somewhat better. However, there are still some holes within the education system that they cannot yet cover. These are my personal views!

Now this is a story, a note, a personal point of view and a perspective I have. Firstly, as I have touched on, I hate broad term labels of learning 'difficulty' or 'disability'. While technically true in word terms, difficulty and disability have what I would call a negative tone and connotation. So – let's look up these words!

Difficulty – (countable, usually plural, uncountable) a problem; a thing or situation that causes problems. (The Oxford English dictionaries.)

Disabilities – a physical or mental condition that limits a persons physical or mental activities.

– a disadvantage or handicap, especially one imposed or recognised by law.

Both of the above, following the word 'learning' are not helpful. They are emotionally demoralising and yes, while they may define dyslexia and dyspraxia combined or singularly they are not good.

The view I take is – Learning challenges.* Also there are NO LIMITS. Just how hard you want to work and push and challenge yourself!!!

Challenges – A new or difficult task or tasks that test someone's abilities and skill. (Oxford English Dictionary)
– An exciting/interesting challenge.
– "The role will be the biggest challenge of his/her acting career."
– To face a challenge (= to have to deal with one)
– "We rose to the challenge, figured out a way to do it."

Doesn't just a small change make a big difference? Yes, with dyslexia or dyspraxia you will find it harder; a struggle at times. But viewing it as a challenge, something to say I can do this, and I will keep trying it until I find a way to do it using a different method until I succeeded in my goal = a win! A positive to give yourself by asking for help or just not giving into it... and practice, practice. Hopefully you get the point.

You pick your label and you set your own "I cans", "I can'ts". You and you alone can choose to ask for help or keep on pushing, and trust me when I literally say - the sky is the limit! (Below - a picture of the C42 light aircraft I can fly. This was my help!)

Top left: Own made label for c42. Bottom is the c42 and the right shows where i stuck the label to remember left and right when called out... did make the instructor a little pale when he saw it 😕 but all went well.

Lastly, I will give this example of a personal label my family, well most of my family gave me. "Oh Alexandar is the 'hands on one'. He can fix things, draw, paint... Bright lad, but he isn't the academic one his younger brother is."

Note, and no offence to my younger brother but when I did return to academic learning, I did 5 A-Levels – pass grades (above his) and went on to do a Foundation Diploma in Art and Design with a Distinction grade. I did all this while holding down a evening and full weekend job.

The 'hands on one'! Ha! Yeah, hands on the bulls horns beating it into submission! The bull would be dyslexia and dyspraxia and the academic system. Don't get me wrong, there were tears, blood, sweat, late nights and tons of swearing (which would have got me a clip around the ear from my ever loving grandmother).

The only ones who didn't view it like this was my maternal grandmother, Constance and my paternal grandfather, Norman.

My grandmother encouraged me to get out of catering 'cheffing' and return to my dream of studying architecture. She taught me a lot in how to be respectful, listen to a different opinion and not react and sometimes even call me up for the crossword answers – I knew the words but still not the spelling. She was an incredibly strict woman. You would not ever dream of back chatting to her but she wanted the best for you. She once said to me, "Alexandar, I want you to be at your best for you and want to see you happy." I won't say too much more. Maybe one day I will write about her, the pages, of course, would have to be script though. She loved letters from me and would write back, even if we had spoken on the phone.

Norman, my grandfather was a 6 foot 1 strongly built man, a naval man, returning home to become a brick layer, a keen rugby player but a true and kind gentleman. He would always be smart, clean shaven and up early, even in retirement.

Once I called myself stupid in front of him and a large heavy hand was placed on my shoulder. "Alexandar you're not stupid. What you've done, it's just not the best way of doing it." He would never put me down. I think he saw potential in me that I was a hard worker and he respected that and in turn I learnt making mistakes was part of not just my life, but everyones. "Best thing you can do is admit it. Hold your hands up and learn from it," he said. He would also love to chat and tell the cheeky comment, joke or story and watching him and my father play Crib, a card game involving a deck of cards and some maths, it was hilarious! They BOTH would move the matchstick up the board, of course accusing the other of cheating. It was good to see and of course, very funny.

I was so lucky in my life to have grandparents like this, I still think of them everyday or on any day a big idea hits me like a tidal wave.

Out of memory lane and about school. Now, in broad terms I hated it. I didn't get the point. Here are some school reports.

Alex does not find the written work aspect of the subject easy but he makes a good effort to answer questions verbally and shows enthusiasm. However, he must be prepared to accept help and support when it is offered as this is how he will make progress.

Teacher: D. Henderson

Year 8 school report on english, first signs

Teacher Comment: Alex is unfailingly cheerful and always lively and perceptive in oral discussion. However, he must not distract himself from what he does not find so easy – getting his ideas down on paper.

Teacher:

Subject Specific Skills	Excellent	Good	Adequate	Poor
SPEAKING AND LISTENING				
Listening and concentrating		✓		
Speaking clearly and confidently			✓	
Co-operating in pairs and groups		✓		
Using imagination			✓	
Improvising			✓	

Teacher Comment: Alex is a very enthusiastic member of the group who is always polite and well-mannered. However, at times he lacks focus; this has resulted in work of varying quality. He must pay attention to the task at all times, not just when he feels like it.

Teacher:

Year 9 school report on english, I was getting bored as you can tell.

Teacher Comment:

Alex can produce work of a good standard both in class and for homework. However this is not always the case, he doesn't always listen and is reluctant to follow new methods carefully. Often he will not accept help and this leads to Alex not understanding some new concepts. He must also learn to respect the right of pupils being able to get on with their work instead, on occasions, of talking to them non-stop.

Year 10 maths report structure issue

Teacher Comment:

Alex has struggled with French throughout the year. For SEN reasons Alex will not be continuing with French in Year 11.

Year 10 French report

Teacher Comment: Alex's concentration varies greatly: sometimes, if he is interested in the subject, he is capable of great insight and sensitivity, but all too often he is distracted. It is vital that he makes the effort to focus fully on each task, and improve the general accuracy of his work which can be very disorganised and untidy. Come on, Alex, you can do better!

Year 11 English report this is where my mother had underlined some key points to be raised wondering why

Teacher Comment:

Alex always works well in lessons and he is very motivated by the prospect of actually making his design in wood, in the mean time he must apply himself to the other parts of his folder. Alex has done some of the work but he seems reluctant to mount this work up and present it for marking. Alex has allowed his work to slip behind schedule and he must apply himself to catching up now. Alex must accept the guidance of his teachers and not be tempted into designing a table that is beyond his skill to make.

Year 11 Design and Technology class. My ideas have always been behind my own personal capability's tick I have found. Later in life I was to learn and surround myself with the right people and keep my ideas streamlined.

As you can see, what they said, was true. I didn't hate all of school. After a lesson there were a few teachers that would hold me back, not because I'd been disruptive or done anything wrong but they had spotted the key thing... something that interested me!

Science – my tutor realised when he spoke about tectonic plates, volcanoes and lightning, even elements, if he put it into more of a story with a description, I would understand it. If I was shown, I could go even further. For example, the massive tectonic plates near San Fransisco moving together. Another would be metals, how they reacted and their structure. This got me interested further. The other things he got me really interested in was rockets. He showed me how to do this safely with a person I was friends with. He knew rockets would be of interest to me as I just wanted to get them higher and faster than planes.

Biology – the human heart. A pump like an engine of a car. I was captivated. He broke down the human body like a car to me. He was a motorbike and car nut job and was able to break down the human body similar to the way you would break down a car and understanding each component combined to make the whole thing work.

Now these two teachers understood something that if I was "liking" the subject taught, my attention would last longer and if I liked an aspect of a subject, I wanted to know more. They did this in their lunch breaks and end of classes and would explain things allowing my privacy to ask, what at the time I thought was a stupid question. The reality in learning is that there is no such thing as a stupid question.

Some other classes I was naturally better at. Art – I could always draw and paint and design technology was the same. Trying to temper down the 100 or so ideas into one that was viably possible was annoying to both my art and design teachers. They did try to though.

Sports (or PE) I loved. However, coordination was hard. Relay, passing the baton or throwing the cricket ball I could never seem to get. Was I left-handed or right? Well practice showed right-handed in the end, but I wasn't a huge fan. The same with swimming. It was so hard to pick up; knowing the way in which my limbs should be moving but running I was good at, and catching. I worked on catching a lot. My PE Teacher wanted me to do two things, catch and run... Rugby, a winger. The only issue he had was my left and right! He once drew with a washable marker, an 'R' on my right hand and an 'L' on my left. He said "This may help and save my throat!" It was a light-hearted joke and also, writing 'R' on my right hand and 'L' on my left was not a bad idea. It even helped me later with swimming and reading a map or listening to directions.

Academically we all know the result. I was put into a newly formed Special Needs class. But the balance and the environment was all wrong. I didn't want to go slower, I just wanted to know.

One last part. I would often go to my school library to play chess. My friend Ahmed from Iran taught me. Once it had finally sunk in which directions and the rules of the pieces, I started to get better at it and play his friends and so on and so on. I could picture in my head his possible moves and then win. He was a kind lad. I always wonder what happened to him. I know he returned to Iran but emails and mobiles didn't exist then, only in the business world.

So, did I hate every bit of school? No. I didn't but times were different. Some things haven't changed and some things have. This was just a little back story of my perspective and time in school. It was the condition (dyslexia and dyspraxia) looked at, not so much the individual with it. It is very different with everyone and it will be with you too. I hope some of this helped. I was just going to jump into the next part but I thought this should be addressed, the good, the bad but also the time frame!

Chapter 6 (Six)

PLANNING AND TIME MANAGEMENT

Planning – To plan a task or tasks like a 'to-do' list.

I personally use this all the while, even with this book. Planning and time management work together hand in hand to maximise your goals and to be as productive as possible.

I find without a day to day plan, things become unstructured. I become disorganised and get off track very quickly.

Time management – planning your time, some basics.

This may sound simple but are key to your goals. You need to work out your needs to be at your most productive and set your own speed.

For me, an example is:

06:00 – wake up.
06:30 – shower + brush teeth.
07:45 – get changed.

08:00 – eat + drink.

08:30 – write up tick box plan of tasks for the day or travel to work.

09:00 – plan written.

17:00 – travel home.

17:30 – change if task required.

18:00 – meal or snack + work out.

19:00 – as above.

20:00 – relax, tv, movie, write, music, etc.

21:00 – brush teeth, dirty clothes in box, fresh clothes ready for next day.

21:45 – bed.

This is a rough guide of a weekday. My added tick box tasks would be things like washing clothes, washing up, emptying bins, walking dogs. Also planning in some fun things like drawing, ideas, painting, jogging a different route, watching reels on Instagram (which is just WAY TO ADDICTIVE!!!) or something bigger like a night out, watching a movie, doing some photos or just going for a drive for an hour to relax my mind.

NOTE – Fail to prepare, prepare to fail. But also try and expect the unexpected. Sometimes the plan has to be thrown out and the day 'scrubbed' but the key is knowing that the person making the timetable can change it. You're in control of your reactions to the unexpected.

To parents – Imposing what is a structure is not what I would advise as the best tactic to take. I would suggest encouragement or suggesting how to streamline a days approach allowing for more free time. Consistency is key for the majors, e.g. waking, eating, self hygiene, bed. A good nights sleep helps the brain and the body and a pattern will form, from my experience, and will work best if slowly adjusted to.

At this point you may be wondering what I have as a structure and how I got into this. Well, as I have said, I was a chef and preparation was key, also preparation for walk-ins (the unexpected). So, that was one of the key factors. Also both my grandfathers were military and would undoubtedly notice if I was scruffy, late or even unshaven and ask why!

What do I plan? Now, I don't want to scare you, but to give context when I left cheffing and went back to college, I was sat in front of an educational psychologist, who with some tests highlighted what dyslexia and dyspraxia meant and how it affected me. Personally, I have what I would call an OCD approach to things and try to find the simplest solution.

So a major component for me was being disorganised, e.g. in both planning and managing my time and money. So, I thought as a chef I would be able to schedule everything, as before that I would forget to wash, eat, pick out clean clothes, or forget a book, the list goes on.

I now have three days a month that I cook food. I then freeze it, then ping (microwave or bake) it to eat and the menu changes with the seasons (spring, summer autumn, winter).

Dressing... I have 3 pairs of the same size jeans and shorts in slightly different colours. I have 3 types of shoes, everyday, sports and smart.

I have an alarm on my phone for drinking/eating. I also keep a diary with two pens, blue and red, with YES tick boxes. Blue has happened (a record) and red is to action. A tick is when it's been completed. I do use black to note words and this also goes everywhere with me.

This is to an extreme, I won't deny it but I met the educational psychologist 3 or so months later to see how I was getting on. I showed her and her mouth dropped. "Okay... I haven't seen that before it really is one extreme to the other with you, isn't it?" she said. I replied, "Yes, well I like to know what's coming and I don't want to, and won't fail at this."

Self-imposed structure to your life isn't a form of captivity, it's freedom. To know you are in control. Structure – the word seems scary, contained, restrained. This isn't how I see it. I call it planning because plans can/will/do change. Knowing how to adapt your plans is good and also your time management so if all goes out the window, you will have a structure (a solid base) to fall back onto.

Tick box tasks – I set myself 6 a day. Why 6? Probably because on the 7th (seventh) day, Sunday – now my rest day, I know what I am doing. I am cooking a roast and watching the Grand Prix then maybe going for a drive. Get out my clothes for Monday and go to bed.

But tick box tasks. 6 of them. 3 of them are must dos, such as take out bins, hoovering, washing up – achievable ones.

That gets you three ticks. Good.

The other 3 more, read about 'X', draw a building, go for an extra 20 minute run.

If I get 2 or 1 out of these 3, it's still good because they're nonessential and it is good to push yourself in a positive way and for something you enjoy.

So say I didn't get to draw a building, that's okay, it goes onto tomorrows tick box list. It's a simple way to set a goal and achieve it using self-determination (setting a goal for yourself – for you, by you)!

Give it a try, see how you get on. Don't try all of it at once. Start with tick boxes.

Last note time – If you are not 10 minutes early, you are going to be late! My misses finds this really annoying, bless! But if I have to be somewhere, I think, "Okay A to B... get in the car 5 minutes, say 20 minutes drive, allow 30 for traffic, 5 minutes to get out the car. 2–3 minutes to get to the exact place... little early? Yes can be, if so listen to some tunes, or check out the menu, write something you've forgotten or learnt, not wasted time."

Summary + note – From this you could start your own plan. Start with basics, getting up on time, getting to be on time.

Tick boxes – just set 3 goals (things you enjoy) want to do or want to try.

You should have got from this chapter:
- some new longer words
- how to plan your time productively
- setting yourself up (preparation)
- managing money
- understanding sometimes it will all just go out the window and go wrong but don't worry, this happens to everyone, regardless of dyslexia or dyspraxia.
- Hopefully now you have a structure to fall on or will do.

NOTE – I also do own other clothes!! A suit and smarter clothes, gym wear etc., but using them at the right time is key!

Chapter 6 completed. [ ] Yes. Bravo ☺

Chapter 7 (Seven)

PHYSICAL EXERCISE AND SPORTS

Making time for physical exercise and sport is important on so many levels. It helps not only in keeping your body fit but also your mind. When you exercise you get a natural release of endorphins and dopamine in your brain making you feel good. It also helps you release stress and relax.

With dyslexia and dyspraxia this also helps in other ways to improve coordination and ups your motivation level given the type of exercise. It can also be social or solitary, e.g. a group activity. If it is with people in a team, this can help with social interaction. It can help you form new social relationships and have a positive emotional impact.

It is also a way to learn that practice makes perfect without being in a high stress environment.

Sports and things that I have tried are scouts, survival courses, rugby, boxing, kick boxing, karate, archery, off road biking, road biking, jogging, cadets, sprinting, skiing, go karting.

Now as I'm a bit older - shooting (both clay and shotgun shooting) and F class rifle sport target shooting, flying, motorbike racing and track days. Swimming and keeping fit still as I have always enjoyed these.

My father and my mother made me or encouraged me to try a lot of these sports or clubs. They all were good fun and showed me new ways to learn and increased my interaction socially outside of the classroom with people of my own age group but also meeting new people from all different walks of life.

If I was to pick my top five and the reason why, they would be:
- Rugby: The group working as a team but knowing your role. Also hand to eye coordination and the positivity and power of a team.
- Flying: This is brilliant. The sense of freedom and such a new discipline (remember the photo?) also flown a P38 warrior... just have to learn.
- Motorbike racing: Okay, parents! Racing, track days. Speed is good fun and such a release of limitations. Plus at track days all the people are just there to have some good fun – plain and simple.
- Jogging: Solitary time. Just at night or very early morning. Time to learn – pacing yourself. 1.2.1.2.1.2. Hearing your feet hit the floor was really relaxing for me.

– Skiing: I learnt to ski on a dry slope. As soon as I was 18, I went to Serbia by myself to ski. I met some amazing people and it was the first of many of my amazing trips alone.

I would recommend all of the sports mentioned or if you're nervous of teams, just by yourself to start. For all of them, it's important for you to enjoy. I think the most two expensive ones are flying and rifle shooting but at the same time, what else do you work for? To do what... find what makes you happy!

Chapter 8 (Eight)

FINDING YOUR SKILL AND WORKING ON IT

What is a skill? – The ability to do something well. Expertise, "difficult work taking great skill".

What is work? - Activity involving mental or physical effort done in order to achieve a purpose or result. "He/she was tired after a days work."

In finding your skill, you also have to take into account 2 other factors.

(1) Enjoyment in your skill vs reward, e.g. pay
(2) Your aspirations of learning a skill. What you can achieve in your current environment? Or does that need to change?

I would first of all pick something you enjoy and form it into your skill by hard work - not dissimilar to a work muscle. Don't just leave it, you keep working at it. You may find you pick up a new skill or a new door will open to you and you may even find you enjoy that too.

My career path you know most of already but I will expand on it. I have only been unemployed for 6 weeks of my working life – I burnt myself out. I had fully reached my maximum, overworked myself, set no boundaries between my home life and my work life, I was socially isolated and drained mentally and physically.

Now this wasn't however my turning point in my life. It was however, a wake up call to set some boundaries, put into place a plan of my day and a routine – "structure".

NOTE – Not the best way to learn but a way of learning and I didn't have a burn out again.

I have had many different jobs. I worked singly as a chef after leaving school thinking, "Well, I'm good at it," so it was a progression into that world. I have however, also been a cleaner, a tree surgeon, a Labrador, ran my own landscaping business for a year to get enough money for my dad's Land Rover and afford driving lessons. I have also worked in a hospital as a hotel customer service assistant. I would take orders, fetch things for patients, empty bins, etc. I have also worked as a cold caller selling windows, data entry for the Kennel Club in an office, ran a night club for a year (12 tills and 20+ staff that I would rather forget), took an early morning paper round, worked as a waiter or chef de rang, also as a bartender. I also worked in an engineering firm starting in the stock room that developed industrial x-ray machines (I loved that job) and I worked for the Post Office while at university going from 9pm to 3am and then university 8am to 5pm. Now, why?

Two things, the first – never be without a job! It doesn't matter what job you have but work hard.

The second, after all these jobs, some offering promotions or better pay, one thing's stuck. I loved architecture but I still had this thought that I was still the 'hands on one' and wasn't smart enough to study architecture.

Well, I had developed a sense of confidence in my last big job before university which was running 3 Bistros (posh pubs!). These served local produce before it was even fashionable. I think I did this well: Managing 3 sites over 60 staff, maintaining the holding stock, watching the wastage was down and seeing to the hiring and firing of staff. Also covering the bar staff, changing the menus, pricing it all up and making sure all of the health and safety and hygiene certificates and forms were up to date. I am proud to say, I did it. Me. The 'hands on one' the 'learning difficulties one' who has to set 'realistic goals' when I said to my form tutor at school that I wanted to study architecture! Well if I can do all that, I can do it. Why not? It's just hard work and I can do that – adapt myself to change.

I first asked my grandmother. She said quickly and with no hesitation, "Well I have never met anyone so hardworking and stubborn, so if you want to, why not Alexandar? It's about time!" While giving me a stern look with a faint smile.

My mind was made up. Also the prospect of having a weekend in the future was nice as in catering you were always working when others were off and off when others were working.

I spoke to both my mother and my father. They both said apprehensively that I should. I had some money saved so I could just about afford it, but I would still have to work 3 nights a week and some weekends to still be, what I would call, fluid with money.

The thing was, where to start? I had no GCSEs and no formal qualification in English or Maths. So I found an engineering college course, a NVQ2 and BTEC 1st Certificate in Engineering. I knew cars, motorbikes and how to fix things. This would be my entry as it counted as 5 GCSEs if passed!! Course work based, practical class size of 10-15 people, okay, I think I can do this... I walked in on the first day, nervous. The first thing I noticed was the whiteboard, full of electrical symbols for capacitors, diodes, resistors, it looked like this...

ELECTRICAL CIRCUIT SYMBOLS DIAGRAM

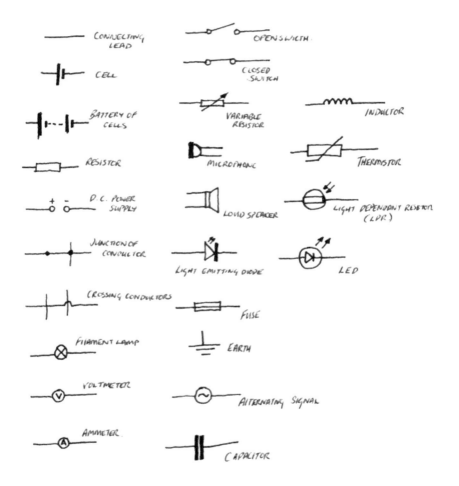

CONNECTING LEAD

CELL

BATTERY OF CELLS

RESISTOR

D.C. POWER SUPPLY

JUNCTION OF CONDUCTOR

CROSSING CONDUCTORS

FILAMENT LAMP

VOLTMETER

AMMETER

OPEN SWITCH

CLOSED SWITCH

VARIABLE RESISTOR

MICROPHONE

LOUD SPEAKER

LIGHT EMITTING DIODE

FUSE

EARTH

ALTERNATING SIGNAL

CAPACITOR

INDUCTOR

THERMISTOR

LIGHT DEPENDANT RESISTOR (LDR.)

LED

My stomach clenched and my heart dropped. Have I just made a huge mistake? Should I go back to my old job... mobile phone, company car, pay rise??

While pondering this, the teacher came out. "Hi, I'm going to teach you the electrical part of this engineering course. Does anybody have any questions?" I had already taken over the front desk and my hand went up. "Okay, I have to ask... What is all that on the whiteboard?"

He explained and described each symbol, name, what it did and how it worked. I loved it! "Wow, I can take this in!" It took my a long while to learn to spell the names of the components, but hand me one and I could tell you what it does and how it works to this day.

So I stuck with it. The English part was the hardest but for me being NVQ based it was - look, copy, repeat by memory. This was not an unfamiliar concept, having been a key method in cheffing. So I used flash cards and kept a book on me at all times. I passed it!

Next I was going to need some A-levels. Well okay, I told my parents again and my grandmother. Keep going... So, interview and a much polished CV plus references and also my new NVQ2 + BTEC 1st certificate in hand, I went for my college interview.

"What would you like to study?" I said, "Maths, Physics, Business, Law and Photography." "Okay well, they're tough subjects." I said, "Well I'm sure I will cope." "Okay. But..." I cut her off. "Don't say 'but'. You just said okay." The admissions officer laughed and said, "You are keen. Okay, you're in. Get ready as you're in for some hard work, Mister."

She wasn't joking.

This is also when I met an educational psychologist (which I spoke of earlier). It was still hard; so, so hard. And the news kept saying that A-levels were getting easier... Like heck!

I must have thrown so many temper tantrums and cried myself to sleep more than once but kept at it and didn't give up.

The hardest was physics. The numbers plus the letters instantly sent me into scramble mode visually. Now I understand physics but I still shudder at the equations.

A year and 6 months later, 3 pass grades but scraped D's on Physics and Law. It was suggested to do a foundation diploma in Art and Design given my (now seriously taken) ambition of studying architecture.

A six foot by six foot model of a town with a 360 degree
view of the town from the centre picture

It was another year and gave me more artistic freedom. I
loved it and I passed with a distinction. My finally protect
was designing a whole town, also filling 4 A2 sketch pads
and drawing a 360 degree panoramic view. I enjoyed it!!

I tell you all of this as the path to finding your skill isn't
a smooth, straight line, but it can be done. I viewed
myself and learning for a long while as pointless with
no practical real world value. This is an incorrect point
of view. I did go on to study architecture and got even
more academic education, but the people and the skills I
learnt along the way were helpful to me both practically
and emotionally.

NOTE – As I said this isn't an autobiography; it is my perspective, my view. I went really the long way round. I don't regret it but I sure have learnt from it.

As you can see finding your skill can, for some, happen earlier. For others it takes time and hard work. You just have to understand that you have to sacrifice time and energy to the process. Having faith in yourself and finding people you trust or who are willing to help you (I certainly needed help, but so do others). For instance, on the final show week of college for my Foundation Diploma, I had worked late into the nights, written work had been done, my big model was done. However, one of my classmates who had done a mostly digital final piece lost all of his work. My tutor came over to me and asked if I could help him basically redo all of his work (she knew I was done). I said yes. I said to him, "What was your project?" He had some notes about graphic design, drawing, using computers. I said, "Okay, get every book from the library that you referenced or used. Bring any and all notes you have and come to my house. We will put on the coffee and piece it all back together."

He could write/type SO fast! It was good. He brought all the books, 20 or so referenced, along with pages of notes and documents.

We first set up a timeline of his project, and over a night and a morning had recreated the whole project. I skimmed the books, found a Post-it Note, ref. 1, ref. 2 and so on. I was now good at finding and identifying useful required information. He would type it up and I would go to the next book or document.

Three pots of coffee and we blew through it. The next day was the show. I did have to have a sleep and set up for the final project! In turn, he redid my logo graphically, which I still use to this day.

This is where I realised I could also take in information at high volumes and found my way of working to maximum efficiency. Music on (no lyrics if writing or reading), books, pens, Post-it Notes to hand, drink and non-messy snacks and away we go.

I had found my working method. Any subject field and task, background noise and prep (e.g. the above) to hand.. I turned into a book information monster eating machine and found my state of flow and learning!

State of flow – In positive psychology, a flow state is where you are fully emerged in what you are doing. I will address this later in emotions and feelings chapter. When you are in a state of flow, you find enjoyment.

Summary – Finding your skill is a progression into something you hopefully enjoy. Accepting the fact that this can change and if it does, be willing to put in the work and change it. It can be done regardless of dyslexia and dyspraxia, just depends on what level of determination you want/need to face!? And lastly be willing to work, or try things out of your comfort zone.

NOTE – To parents. Finding some things your child enjoys is paramount and expanding on a chosen subject field is a positive approach.

Example – If its art, well why is red, red and its meaning? Same for blue? Why is the sky blue but at night, black? In that, you can cover emotional reactions, chemical processes, elements, astrology and nature. The black sky = astrology and nature, and biology factors as well… cool how its all linked!

NOTE – To parents and reader! What links to your enjoyment? Want to make it a skill? Practice at it. Try. Don't be scared to make mistakes. Take a chance. The path won't always be easy but where will it take you? You won't know if you don't try. Regardless of dyslexia and dyspraxia, it's the same for everyone!

Just remember if trying something new to plan time, keep a job, don't over jump, e.g. try it all at once. Try it at weekends or free time. See where you go with it.

P.S. Eight!! I FORGOT how to spell it! I actually had to look it up. In the chapter, 'Refreshing skills', I will address this and explain why! 🤕

Chapter 9 (nine)
– Ha, I can spell that one!

WORKING, LEARNING, METHODS AND SETTING

Start with a note – Things may take longer to learn but if you take your time, you will pick them up. It shows not just to yourself, that you have commitment, determination and passion but to others too. It also shows to yourself and others (if it is family or employers) you are able to adapt yourself to a challenge and your 'labels' won't hold you back.

Setting and setting up your working and learning area for yourself is key to productive learning. Also the environment you are in, e.g. Are you reading/listening to this in your room, living room, a park, the library? On a long journey or studying? What spaces have you found you are most comfortable in? Which one or ones are you most happy in?

Another component to this is – do you enjoy background noise or not? Or can you keep your concentration up if someone were to ask a question or not?

Lastly, in the previous chapters, I touched on your set up. Do you have to hand paper, a notepad, pen, pencil, rubber, highlighter? Or tons of Post-it Notes! "I HAVE AN ADDICTION TO THEM!"

NOTE – It is all a variable balancing act however, try to find your comfort zone. Try different ways until you get there. What works for me, may not work for you and vice versa. So that is your set up and environment. (Preparation).

For instance when making the framework for the planning of this book, I was at my desk, TV on in the background and I was jotting away on many, many Post-its.

When I was going further into detail, e.g. what I wanted in bullet point questions, I would write headings and a rough note. Now penning them out neatly I was listening to music, in a hospital waiting room, at my desk and once in bed!

Now when writing these chapters expanding on my bullet points, I was at my desk in the mornings at 07:00 with a coffee until about 10:30. Sometimes with music but no screens. The same in the evenings if I had thought of something or to add in or wanted to word it differently.

I found I would think about a chapter as a whole that centres around 5-6 points that I wanted to make and how I wanted to translate that information to you, the reader.

These were my methods just on this book.

I did plan my time, I did get interrupted by my Labradors MANY TIMES! ☺ or my phone ☹ – That quickly went on silent but sadly I haven't found the mute button for Labradors... haha

There are many new methods and ways of approaching learning or working. It isn't a 'one size fits all'. It is like a new pair of shoes. Sometimes you get the right size and fit but they are still stiff and new; not comfortable yet. But a week later however, they fit like a glove (which ironically goes on your hand!!). They fit! You don't throw them away or return them after a day or 2, you give them a little time. You pick up if the fit is right.

Summary

- Find your place.
- Find your set up.
- Adapt your method.

And away we go. Remember that as you progress you can also change and you may also have to change if you are not happy with your progression. But a safe space, comfort and time are the big elements to this.

Handy tips:
- Listing your tasks
- Tick box approach
- Revisit notes
- Expanding on a word and its meaning
- Setting your focus on a subject you enjoy
- What links you to your subject?
- Identify things that hold you back then remove.
- Don't give up. Allow yourself TIME to settle.

Chapter 10 (Ten)

VERBAL AND NON-VERBAL COMMUNICATION

Verbal communication and non-verbal is very important and has varying factors, as you are dealing with different people, different situations and different social settings.

The 'big one' – speaking correctly. Now we don't need to speak like we have been brought up in the Royal Household, however we do want to sound clear, confident and precise in the way we talk!

Now, I personally have to think before I speak. Like reading, I can jump a line or misread or 'jumble' a word, and the point I was trying to make, however valid, becomes watered down somewhat. Or I try to go as fast as I can think and then get in a right old muddle and then forget what I wanted to say!

How do I face this little annoyance? Well, it depends on the situation but in broad stroke terms, I slow down. Not so that I sound slow, but I set a pace to what I am saying. Second, if in conversation or discussion, an idea will hit me and I will have to note it down instead of blurting it out. It helps me to be clear and not jumble the way I want to make my point.

Reading aloud is hard. I generally try to avoid it. If it can be practiced, I practice, yes... over and over and over.

The scary part – I have and do catch myself doing this... having full blown conversations with myself, playing not only myself but the other person. I guess their questions and formulate my answers, or replies (ha). My mother and my partner have seen this first hand! I guess it is a little odd but 9 times out of 10, it works!

NOTE – Hehe... so a couple of cheats to give you. Time, if you get lost for words in general conversation. Reply back with interest by repeating their last statement and make it a question...

Take a drink of water, ask them to repeat. "Sorry, I didn't quite catch that" and two very sneaky ones – I cough or pretend to sneeze and they will forget what they were saying and say, "Pardon" or "Bless you" and this gives you time.

Another smaller story is, during lockdown I started playing piano (teaching myself). I did this not because I was bored but because I had been reading a book by David Eagleman about the brain. Why did I read this book? Nothing about dyslexia or dyspraxia, I just found myself interested in the brain.

One aspect this book talked about was forming new neural pathways in the brain and how they could grow and reinforce like tree roots, both with good and bad! The more you learn a subject the stronger the root and the pathway becomes bigger and lasts longer. It also spoke about using both hemispheres of the brain, e.g. the left and the right side and the impacts were interesting as I wanted to move both hands in time together, using both sides of my brain.

I downloaded a piano playing app and learnt a few bits. I then went to put fingers on keys... I'd miss a note. I just keep trying, left hand again trying and trying. Then both hands together and it started to sink in. Also by using a timing app on my phone called a metronome I was able to speed up with both hands and keep in time.

It was and still is an interest/hobby of mine and I learnt a lesson – keeping in time is what can be applied to my speech or the way I speak.

The English language is rather 'sing-song'. The way we pronounce words with tone and timing. No different to playing musical keys; words to form a sentence, a melody would be a paragraph.

All timing, all practice and a simple lesson learnt and better coordination between left and right hand! I can now write with both, catch with both and keep in time dancing to music (something I never understood before!!!).

Applied to verbal communication, the learning pattern can be the same: Think.... Read the music, e.g. think of the words, note the tempo - the speed you need to be clear. Then play the music! Allow your voice to pronounce the notes, e.g. words, to make the tune clear and correct like the music would be.

Music = think – read the music – remember the tempo – play
Speaking = think – words – note the speed you need to be clear – speak

Key things to take away:
– Take time to think before you speak, what you are going to say and how you are going to say it
– Other helpful tasks to train your brain to mouth communication – read out loud simple children's poems or books and tongue twisters to challenge yourself.
– Lastly, pronouncing words with silent letters, such as 'Ph' sounds like 'f' in physics.

Next look at the words as pictures, describe something instead of trying to explain it. Same thing, very different results. It also engages conversation about your chosen subject.

Tell a story to make a point can be helpful! Also being engaging and clear, it's easier to remember. But as I say, this is how I have found it to be. It can be different!

Lastly, how you choose to say something and judging your social setting. For instance, is it casual or formal? Is it a discussion, an argument or just a chat? Now, judging these situations is only done with practice but always bear in mind, conversations and topics can change from a casual manner to a more serious one. Remembering the topic and setting is key, but remember everybody can still get caught out!

Have you ever heard this...
"It's not what you said,
it's the way you said it!"

Now I have, many times! It's normally because my tone is not suited for the situation or I have spoken too fast and can be to direct which can be perceived as confrontational.

I also have adopted a very direct speaking style, mostly on the phone as I REALLY don't like repeating myself! So how do I not offend people? I simply say or state that I find it easier to be direct and it has no bearing on my current mood. I sometimes adopt this in casual meetings or social situations if the topic in question becomes serious.

"Forgive me, but I like to speak directly, e.g. to the point, as sometimes I get lost. How I have said it, isn't how I mean it."

This allows the other person to understand you are removing emotion from the wording and the way you speak. It also explains without saying, I have dyslexia and dyspraxia. So this is easier for me and could be for you, to understand verbal communication. For example, "Forgive me. I tend to be quite direct, I am not angry, I am to the point."

Non-verbal communication, a shrug of the shoulders, a tilt of the head or the hands palms up waist high can be an expression of 'I don't know. Maybe?' It varies from person to person.

Another is facial expression, which regardless of gender or race, are all the same. However, you have to be able to accept these and understand the context when they are made. The hit US TV show, Lie To Me, is an easy watch based on a really good book by Dr Paul Ekman, called Emotions Revealed. I will reference this book in the next chapter as it made me realise some things that were really helpful.

Understanding non-verbal communication is important. The way someone is holding themselves. Is it arms crossed, leaning head on a palm? These are just a few examples of body language. Knowing these can help you control yours and can help. You can describe with your hands. This can aid in describing a point or by default, explain it and put passion into what you are saying.

Also some commonly used hand signals (NOT WHAT YOU THINK!! ☺😄) you will have noticed can sometimes give yourself time, or a way of expressing yourself with these...

Are you okay? All good. I don't know! Wait... thought... question? Heart – Love you ♥, Hi... bye.

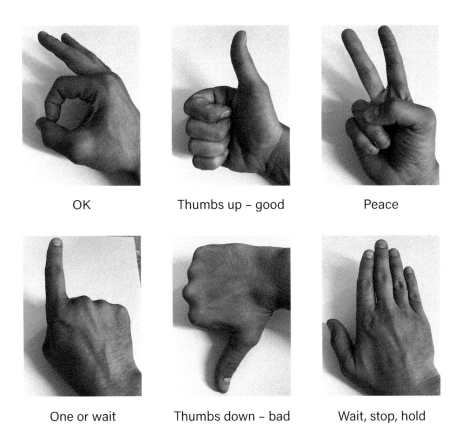

OK	Thumbs up – good	Peace
One or wait	Thumbs down – bad	Wait, stop, hold

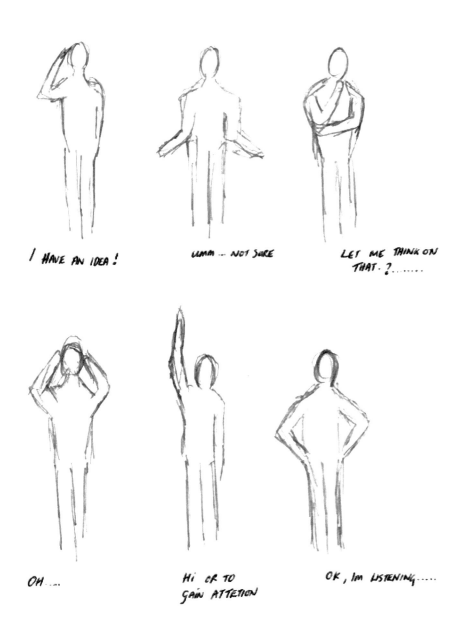

Chapter 11 (eleven)

EMOTIONS AND FEELINGS

You will feel – NO, stop there… everyone is different. Everyone reacts with dyslexia and dyspraxia in a different way. What IS important is knowing what you COULD be feeling – you, yourself, you. Then being able to safely express those feelings in a clear and concise way to other people should you need or wish to.

NOTE – To parents. Emotions and dyslexia and dyspraxia can be very fluid things to deal with. The main part is to be supportive by listening. While you may not ever be fully able to understand why your child feels or reacts like they do, you can accept there are different ways that we all think and approach things. A good reference is Carl Rogers – thinking about positive acceptance.

NOTE – To reader. There are some common emotions you COULD be feeling with your dyslexia and dyspraxia, and certainly ones that I have felt, but that doesn't mean you will. But being informed of the possible is, I think a good forewarning. Frustration, anger, jealousy, annoyance, self doubt, anxiety and depression. I think I have felt all f these at some point or another, even some while writing this book!!

My path when I was younger (10–16), included frustration, anger and a lot of self doubt. And when I had tests – a lot of anxiety and after tests, jealousy and annoyance at myself and jealousy towards others for seeming able to do it all so easily.

Moving forward (15-20s) I learned to channel my anger. My selfdoubt with work would become less as I had built up my confidence by people I worked with in cheffing encouraging me. This also was coupled with sports, boxing, rugby and running. Why? Well you can loose control but you take more hits and lose a match in boxing. In rugby, (coined not by me) 'a yob sport played by gentleman', means there is an understanding that the explosive aggression required stays on the pitch but also channelled with your team mates and coach. Now running – an escape, a way to almost meditate. Just focus on a simple task, put one foot in front of the other. This allowed my brain to relax. To some extent I also when running, would problem solve subconsciously.

In college, around my A-levels, a lot of these emotions crept back in. Why? Because I was taxing my brain and I can say I had never given my emotions much notice (not healthy).

I was given a book that really opened my eyes. Not a complex read, called 'Emotions Revealed' by Paul Ekman. In short, I wish I had read this 10 years earlier! It helped explain why I reacted the way I did. Also trigger points that would make me angry and that would open up the flood gates of emotions. It is really worth a read.

I still struggle – well, work on my emotions. I say that head held high and no shame. I scream into a pillow sometimes and did when writing this! I also hit the gym to break a sweat and focus on a simple task. I will also go out for a walk or night drive just to clear my head if I have had a hard day.

Another interesting challenge which I still face is decision making and impulse control. The impulse purchase and the decision to do something and in what order – like this book! I was unsure on how to structure the last 5 chapters, I had planned them differently, but as I spoke of allowing the possibility of change to happen, I restructured the chapters before penning them out.

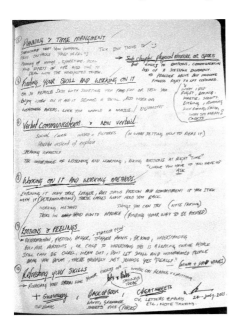

I live by a motto. I believe I made it up, which is:
"Aim for the best, plan for the worst,
and hope for the happy middle!"

<u>Aim for the best</u> – plan, work hard, determination, holding yourself to the highest standard possible.

<u>Plan for the worst</u> – plan for what may be the pitfalls. Where are the weaknesses in your plan? What are the bad outcomes? Can you do anything to avoid them?

<u>Hope for the happy middle</u> – set yourself for a middle ground. An outcome that you could be happy with. Maybe you didn't get the A, but you got the C – you still passed! You had faith and did your best so your head can be held high regardless of the result if you gave it your all!

Be prepared to understand it sometimes just goes wrong! But if you need to, you can try again, pick up, dust off and keep on pushing! Never be afraid to ask for help or express your emotions. I buried mine for years. Not healthy but I thought it was the way to be. What I have learnt was to find someone, a family member, a friend you trust or a trained psychologist to sound off how you are feeling and why that might be.

NOTE – To parents. A child or young person may do this and start to push these negative feelings inwards. Sometimes, as I say, being able to voice them without judgment is sometimes really just SO valuable!

Another somewhat sad aspect is bullying, or being made fun of, or being the butt of a joke. Two ways I approach this depending on the ituation, I laugh it off or I address it as most often it is a stupid comment but still usually said by a uninformed person. Not dwelling on them is important. You don't have to justify it, explain it or let it get to you but the choice/judgement of the situation is yours.

People can still be cruel and unkind. I have found personally, this comes when they are actually jealous of you and your abilities. Don't let them drag you down. It will actually annoy them more by not giving a reaction. Walk away, head high. You just removed a problem by offering zero reaction!

I could go on about psychology and learning but I believe the key building blocks required are here to summarise it:
- Does it make you feel bad? – Yes/No?
  You can remove it or learn from it.
- Have you taken on too much? - Yes/No?
  You can take a step back or ask for help.
- Are you struggling with a wave of negative emotion? Yes/No?
  What is the cause? What is the effect on you? Can you Talk to someone? Can you write it down and learn from it?

Examine your safe people – your circle of friends and family, do they understand? Can you explain? Or can you describe how it makes you feel? Or can someone else help, like a teacher or a psychologist?

It is a constant state of self-reflection and evaluation of yourself. Start small. Don't react. Allow yourself time to process what you are feeling. Occupy your time. Never give up on yourself and it is not over.

I have focused mainly on the things that can make you feel negative. That is because when dealing with dyslexia and dyspraxia, they sink in the most and are more easily noted. However emotions, like enjoyment and satisfaction in completing a task and a sense of achievement, are things that you should actively look out for and take note of when you find them.

In your comfort learning zone you may find yourself in a state of flow. This is brilliant. I get now under multiple pressures and find it easier to cope with more than one thing. It means that you are in the zone, focused on your task or tasks, fully immersed. I get this in sports as much as academically within the right setting now.

Be proud of your achievements even if it is something small. Also if you didn't give up but didn't get the result you wanted, you demonstrated courage, endurance, commitment and passion!

Chapter 12 (twelve)

REFRESHING YOUR SKILLS!

Eight! Eight! Eight! ... Yes I forgot!!! How to spell this word and a few others. A bit like skiing, riding a bike or even roller blading. If you haven't don't it in a while, you will forget things! It's not lazy, it's just something you have to keep on top of and refresh from time to time. No harm in it.

Refreshing your brain! Instead of a night of Netflix, pick up a book!!

For instance, I LOVE to rewatch movies. I was going to rewatch the movie 'The Martian' again. I love it. I love sci-fi but instead I decided to get the book! It was brilliant, an easy read and an audiobook! The same for 'The Hobbit' and the Harry Potter books, also both with audio!

Stephen Fry's books are good with audio though as I said before – longer words!! Post-it Notes required! But brilliant!

Lastly, there are many audiobooks out there. Pick up unabridged (word for word) and what you enjoy - fiction, non-fiction, TV, films? I find generally the same applies to the books. You can also get these for free or low cost from the library or school, even Audible give a 3 free book trial.

Have a go at penmanship (handwriting). See it as an art form, create your own?

The main thing is enjoyment in what you are doing for all of the above!

Summary

This book has taken me back and forward. I hope along the way you have picked up some new words and understand them. It is just a process and finding what fits you.

Hopefully you won't make some of the mistakes, or should I say learning curves, as I have. However, I have learnt from them.

I still am learning myself. Gathering new information all the time, I try new things. Will you?

Already you have with this book, a first for us both! Keep at it and yep, look in the back for the answers!

Finding what you need is not a bad thing at all. Enjoy!

Back of the Book

WORDS AND THEIR MEANING

– from the Oxford Advanced Learner's Dictionary

intelligence
noun

the ability to learn, understand and think in a logical way about things; the ability to do this well
- a person of high/average/low intelligence
- He didn't even have the intelligence to call for an ambulance.
- As a director, he tends to underestimate the intelligence of his audience.
- Please don't insult my intelligence by lying to me.

categories
noun

a group of people or things with particular features in common SYNONYM class
- These are the nominees from each category.

- in a category He competed in the youngest age category.
- Students over 25 fall into a different category.
- The results can be divided into three broad categories.
- It is not useful to divide schoolchildren into separate categories.
- The film doesn't fit into any specific category.
- by category You can filter the results by category.

misinformed
verb

to give somebody wrong information about something
- be misinformed (about something) They were deliberately misinformed about their rights.
- The parents had been misinformed about the incident.
- a misinformed belief (= based on wrong information)

commitment
noun

[countable, uncountable] a promise to do something or to behave in a particular way; a promise to support somebody/ something; the fact of committing yourself
- I'm not ready to make a long-term commitment.
- They have failed to honour their commitments.
- commitment to somebody/something The company has shown a commitment to diversity over the years.

- He questioned the government's commitment to public services.
- We're looking for a firm commitment from both sides.
- commitment to do/doing something This project demonstrates our commitment to improving the quality of the city's green spaces.
- They reaffirmed their commitment to work for peace.
- commitments under something Australia is determined to meet its commitments under the agreement.inspiration

adapt
verb

[intransitive, transitive] to change your behaviour in order to deal more successfully with a new situation
SYNONYM adjust
- It's amazing how soon you adapt.
- The organisms were forced to adapt in order to survive.
- adapt to something Some animals have a remarkable ability to adapt to changing environments.
- A large organisation can be slow to adapt to change
- The company was able to adapt to the conditions and enhance its position.
- We have had to adapt quickly to the new system.
- adapt yourself to something It took him a while to adapt himself to his new surroundings.

pronounce

verb

transitive] pronounce something to make the sound of a word or letter in a particular way
- to pronounce a word/syllable/vowel/consonant
- Very few people can pronounce my name correctly.
- The 'b' in lamb is not pronounced.
- I found it difficult to pronounce the name of the port.

communication

noun

[uncountable] the activity or process of expressing ideas and feelings or of giving people information
- communication between A and B Good communication between team leaders and members is essential.
- communication with somebody attempts to improve communication with customers
- The campaign will appear across all communication channels.
- helping students develop their communication skills
- non-verbal communication such as gestures or facial expressions
- in communication We are in regular communication by email.unabridged

interested

adjective

giving your attention to something because you enjoy finding out about it or doing it; showing interest in something and finding it exciting

- He sounded genuinely interested.
- interested in something/somebody I'm very interested in history.
- I'm not particularly interested in art.
- interested in doing something Anyone interested in joining the club should contact us at the address below.
- interested to do something We would be interested to hear your views on this subject.
- an interested audience
- She was watching with a politely interested expression on her face.
- There's a talk on Italian art—are you interested (= would you like to go)?

inaccurate

adjective

not exact or accurate; with mistakes

- an inaccurate statement
- We can't base a forecast on inaccurate information.
- All the maps we had were wildly inaccurate.

- Statistical graphs may be inaccurate and misleading.
OPPOSITE accurate

fundamental
adjective

serious and very important; affecting the most central and important parts of something
SYNONYM basic
- the fundamental principles of scientific method
- You have a fundamental right to privacy.
- a fundamental question/problem/issue
- a question of fundamental importance
- This principle is absolutely fundamental.
- There is a fundamental difference between the two points of view.
- A fundamental change in the organisation of health services was required.

conversation
noun

an informal talk involving a small group of people or only two; the activity of talking in this way
- a phone conversation
- The main topic of conversation was the likely outcome of the election.

- I tried to make conversation (= to speak in order to appear polite).
- conversation with somebody I had a long conversation with her the other day.
- She was engaged in conversation with a colleague.
- (British English) to get into conversation with somebody
- (North American English) to get into a conversation with somebody
- conversation between A and B I overheard a conversation between two colleagues.
- conversation about something We had to listen to endless conversations about high prices and food shortages.
- in conversation Don was deep in conversation with the girl on his right.
- I spent an hour in conversation with him.
- The conversation turned to gardening.

Encouragement
noun

the act of encouraging somebody to do something; something that encourages somebody
- a few words of encouragement
- He needs all the support and encouragement he can get.
- With a little encouragement from his parents he should do well.

- encouragement (to somebody) (to do something)
  She was given every encouragement to try something new.
- Her words were a great encouragement to them.

OPPOSITE discouragement

approaches

noun

[countable] a way of dealing with somebody/something; a way of doing or thinking about something such as a problem or a task
- She took the wrong approach in her dealings with them.
- It was time to take a different approach.
- an alternative/innovative approach
- a traditional/similar approach
- The approach they were using no longer seemed to work.
- approach to something We need to adopt a new approach to the problem.
- The therapy takes a holistic approach to health and well-being.
- approach for something a variety of approaches for the treatment of depression
- approach for doing something Will this be a successful approach for providing high-tech offices?

practice

noun

[uncountable, countable] doing an activity or training regularly so that you can improve your skill; the time you spend doing this

- conversation practice
- It takes a lot of practice to play the violin well.
- There's a basketball practice every Friday evening.
- She does an hour's piano practice every day.
- with practice With practice you will become more skilled.
- practice in doing something I've had a lot of practice in saying 'no' recently!
- It takes years of practice to get it right.
- We had an extra practice session on Friday.

fluently

adverb

if you speak a language or read fluently, you speak or read easily and well

- She speaks German fluently.
- a child just beginning to read fluently

calligraphy

noun

beautiful handwriting that you do with a special pen or brush;
the art of producing this
- a poem written in neat italic calligraphy

combination

noun

[countable] two or more things joined or mixed together to
form a single unit
- combination of something The tragedy was due to a
  combination of factors.
- They recommend reducing expenditure, increasing
  taxes, or a combination of the two.
- his unique combination of skills
- His treatment was a combination of surgery, radiation
  and drugs.
- What an unusual combination of flavours!
- Try different combinations of exotic fruit in a fresh fruit
  salad.
- The best approach may well be to use a combination of
  both methods.
- Technology and good management. That's a winning
  combination (= one that will certainly be successful).

abbreviations

noun

abbreviation (of/for something) a short form of a word, etc.
- AC is the standard abbreviation for 'air conditioning.'
- Abbreviations are used in the text to save space.
- Ad lib is an abbreviation of the Latin phrase 'ad libitum.'
- The abbreviation PC stands for 'personal computer.'

compared

verb

[transitive] to examine people or things to see how they are similar and how they are different
- compare A and B It is interesting to compare their situation and ours.
- We compared the two reports carefully.
- The internet allows you to compare prices from a variety of companies.
- How can you compare the two things? They are so different!
- Compare and contrast the characters of Jack and Ralph.
- compare A with/to B We compared the results of our study with those of other studies.
- My own problems seem insignificant compared with other people's.

- I've had some difficulties, but they were nothing compared to yours (= they were not nearly as bad as yours).
- Standards in healthcare have improved enormously compared to 40 years ago.
- They receive just over three years of schooling, compared to a national average of 7.3.
- an increase of over 11% compared to the same period last year

Remember

verb

[transitive, intransitive] to have or keep an image in your memory of an event, a person, a place, etc. from the past
- remember somebody/something This is Carla. Do you remember her?
- I don't remember my first day at school.
- I'll always remember this holiday.
- She doesn't remember a thing about it.
- She fondly remembered her early years in India.
- remember somebody/something as something He still remembered her as the lively teenager he'd known years before.
- remember somebody/something from something I remember her from university .

- remember somebody/something with something He will be remembered with affection by all who knew him.
- As far as I can remember, this is the third time we've met.
- remember doing something I remember seeing pictures of him when I was a child.
- Do you remember switching the lights off before we came out?
- I remember thinking what a brilliant idea that was.
- I remember reading something in the paper about that.
- I remember watching the film on television.

assortment
noun

a collection of different things or of different types of the same thing
SYNONYM mixture
- a wide assortment of gifts to choose from
- He was dressed in an odd assortment of clothes.
- an assortment of plates of varying sizes

vocabulary
noun

[countable, uncountable] all the words that a person knows or uses
- to have a wide/limited vocabulary

- your active vocabulary (= the words that you use)
- your passive vocabulary (= the words that you understand but don't use)
- Reading will increase your vocabulary.

management
noun

[uncountable] the activity of running and controlling a business or similar organisation
- a career in management
- hotel/project management
- a management training course
- the day-to-day management of the business
- The report blames bad management.
- Effective financial management is essential.
- The company's top-down management style made decision-making slow and inflexible.

components
noun

one of several parts of which something is made
- the different organizations involved in the design of the various components
- component of something Key components of the government's plan are...

- an essential/important component of something
- a major/principal/critical component of something
- Nitrogen is the main component of air.
- The country still lacks the basic components of a real democratic system.
- the components of a machine
- component for something Individual components for the car can be very expensive.
- component in something Trust is a vital component in any relationship.

Consistency
noun

[uncountable] (approving) the quality of always behaving in the same way or of having the same opinions, standard, etc.; the quality of being consistent
- She has played with great consistency all season.
- We need to ensure the consistency of service to our customers.

OPPOSITE inconsistency

suspicion
noun

[uncountable, countable] a feeling that somebody has done something wrong, illegal or dishonest, even though you have no proof

- They drove away slowly to avoid arousing suspicion.
- on suspicion of something He was arrested on suspicion of murder.
- suspicion that... I have a sneaking suspicion that she's not telling the truth.
- My suspicions were confirmed when police raided the property.
- She was reluctant to voice her suspicions.
- His resignation seemed only to fuel suspicions.
- It's time to confront him with our suspicions.

advantages

noun

a thing that helps you to be better or more successful than other people
- a distinct/significant/huge advantage
- It gives you an unfair advantage (= something that benefits you, but not your opponents).
- She had the advantage of a good education.
- You will be at an advantage (= have an advantage) in the interview if you have thought about the questions in advance.
- advantage over somebody The company was able to gain a competitive advantage over its rivals by reducing costs.
- Being tall gave him an advantage over the other players.

OPPOSITE disadvantage

Ironically
adverb

in a way that shows that you really mean the opposite of what you are saying; in a way that expresses irony
- He smiled ironically.

progress
noun

the process of improving or developing, or of getting nearer to achieving or completing something
- I think we're making progress.
- We will continue to monitor progress over the next few months.
- economic/scientific/technological progress
- rapid/good progress
- We hope to see some real progress by March.
- progress in something James is making steady progress in his recovery.
- progress in doing something Police are making significant progress in fighting computer crime.
- The two sides have made very slow progress in resolving the dispute.
- progress on something There's been no sign of progress on this issue.

- progress towards something The company is making progress towards this target.
- They asked for a progress report on the building work.

confident
adjective

feeling sure about your own ability to do things and be successful
- She was in a relaxed, confident mood.
- Beneath his confident and charming exterior, lurked a mass of insecurities.
- confident about something I was actually fairly confident about my chances.
- confident about doing something The teacher wants the children to feel confident about asking questions when they don't understand.
- confident in something He'd learned to be confident in his ability to handle anything life threw at him.

engaged
adjective

having agreed to marry somebody
- When did you get engaged?
- an engaged couple
- engaged to somebody She's engaged to Peter.

- They are engaged to be married (= to each other).
- I can't come to dinner on Tuesday—I'm otherwise engaged (= I have already arranged to do something else).
- engaged in something They were engaged in conversation.
- to be engaged in dialogue/discussion/debate
- They are engaged in talks with the Irish government.
- engaged on something She is actively engaged on several projects.

increases
verb

to become greater in amount, number, value, etc.; to make something greater in amount, number, value, etc.
- Costs have increased significantly.
- to increase dramatically/substantially
- The price of oil increased.
- increase in something Oil increased in price.
- increase by something The rate of inflation increased by 2 per cent.
- increase from A to B The population has increased from 1.2 million to 1.8 million.
- increase with something Disability increases with age (= the older somebody is, the more likely they are to be disabled).

- increase something Sun exposure may increase the risk of skin cancer.
- Our aim is to increase the number of women in the sport.
- The company plans to significantly increase product availability over the next year.
- increase something by something They've increased the price by 50 per cent.
- increase something from A to B Last month the reward was increased from $20 000 to $40 000.
- An increasing number of people live alone.
- increasing levels of carbon dioxide in the earth's atmosphere

OPPOSITE decrease

Identifying
verb

to recognise somebody/something and be able to say who or what they are

- identify somebody/something She was able to identify her attacker.
- Passengers were asked to identify their own suitcases before they were put on the plane.
- identify yourself Many of those arrested refused to identify themselves (= would not say who they were).

- identify somebody/something as somebody/something
  The bodies were identified as those of two suspected drug dealers.
- identify somebody/something by something two species of waterbirds that can be identified by their distinctive beaks

sentences

noun

[countable] (grammar) a set of words expressing a statement, a question or an order, usually containing a subject and a verb. In written English sentences begin with a capital letter and end with a full stop/period (.), a question mark (?) or an exclamation mark (!).
- Does the sentence contain an adverb?
- I was too stunned to finish my sentence.
- There are mistakes in grammar, sentence structure and punctuation.
- Let's take that paragraph apart sentence by sentence.

hindsight

noun

the understanding that you have of a situation only after it has happened and that means you would have done things in a different way

- with hindsight With hindsight it is easy to say they should not have released him.
- in hindsight What looks obvious in hindsight was not at all obvious at the time.
- It's easy to criticise with the benefit of hindsight.

recognised
verb

to know who somebody is or what something is when you see or hear them or it, because you have seen or heard them or it before
- recognise somebody/something I recognised him as soon as he came in the room.
- Do you recognise this tune?
- You might not recognise the name but you'll know her face.
- I recognised the voice immediately.
- recognise somebody/something by something I recognised her by her red hair.
- recognise somebody/something from something I recognised him from the photo in the paper.

succeeded
verb

[intransitive] to achieve something that you have been trying to do or get; to have the result or effect that was intended

- Our plan succeeded.
- Whether we succeed or fail depends on ingenuity and luck.
- succeed in doing something He succeeded in getting a place at art school.
- I tried to discuss it with her but only succeeded in making her angry (= I failed and did the opposite of what I intended).

OPPOSITE fail (1)

Distinction

noun

[countable] distinction (between A and B) a clear difference or contrast especially between people or things that are similar or related

- distinctions between traditional and modern societies
- Philosophers did not use to make a distinction between arts and science.
- We need to draw a distinction between the two events.
- [countable, uncountable] a special mark or award that is given to somebody, especially a student, for excellent work
- Naomi got a distinction in maths.
- with distinction He graduated with distinction.

academic
adjective

[usually before noun] connected with education, especially studying in schools and universities
- high/low academic standards
- She had a brilliant academic career.
- one of this country's most prestigious academic institutions
- improving the academic achievement of all students
- The university is renowned throughout the world for its academic excellence.
- academic research/researchers
- We are deeply committed to safeguarding academic freedom.

crossword
noun

a game in which you have to fit words across and downwards into spaces with numbers in a square diagram. You find the words by solving clues.
- to do a/the crossword
- I've finished the crossword apart from 3 across and 10 down.

description
noun

a piece of writing or speech that says what somebody/
something is like; the act of writing or saying in words what
somebody/something is like
- Follow the link below for a more detailed description.
- description of somebody/something a brief description
  of the software
- The name means 'no trees' and it is an accurate
  description of the island.
- Police have issued a description of the gunman.
- This is a film that defies description (= is difficult or
  impossible to describe).
- the novelist's powers of description
- beyond description a personal pain that goes beyond
  description (= is too great to express in words)

environment
noun

the environment [singular] the natural world in which people,
animals and plants live
- The government should do more to protect the
  environment.
- to preserve/pollute/harm the environment
- damage to the natural environment

- protection/destruction of the marine environment
- The environment minister expressed concern over pollution levels.

business

noun

[uncountable, singular] the activity of making, buying, selling or supplying goods or services for money
SYNONYM commerce, trade

- It's been a pleasure to do business with you.
- There will be some changes to the way we conduct business.
- in business She has set up in business as a hairdresser.
- When he left school, he went into business with his brother.
- the music/entertainment/movie business
- the insurance/banking business
- the food/restaurant/hotel business
- Retail is a tough business.
- in the... business She works in the software business.
- We need to concentrate on our core business (= the main thing that our business does).
- business owners/leaders
- a business partner
- the business community

maximise

verb

maximise something to increase something as much as possible
- to maximise efficiency/fitness/profits
- (computing) Maximise the window to full screen.

unstructured

adjective

without structure or organisation
- an unstructured interview

disorganised

adjective

badly planned; not able to plan or organise well
- It was a hectic disorganised weekend.
- She's so disorganised.
- Don't expect him to get there on time—he's completely disorganised.

prepare

verb

[transitive, intransitive] to make something or somebody ready to be used or to do something
- prepare something/somebody to prepare a report

- prepare something/somebody for somebody/something A hotel room is being prepared for them.
- The college prepares students for a career in business.
- prepare somebody/something to do something The training has prepared me to deal with any medical issue.
- prepare for something We all set about preparing for the party.

psychologist
noun

a scientist who studies and is trained in psychology
- to see a psychologist
- to go to a psychologist
- an educational psychologist
- a clinical psychologist (= one who treats people with mental disorders or problems)
- I made an appointment with the school psychologist.
- a child psychologist
- a sports psychologist

schedule
noun

[countable, uncountable] a plan that lists all the work that you have to do and when you must do each thing
- I have a hectic schedule for the next few days.

- a busy/gruelling/punishing schedule
- We're working to a tight schedule (= we have a lot of things to do in a short time).
- He has taken some time out of his busy schedule to talk to us.
- They have a very flexible work schedule.
- I have no time available in my regular schedule.
- on schedule Filming began on schedule (= at the planned time).
- The project will be completed on schedule this summer.
- ahead of schedule The new bridge has been finished two years ahead of schedule.
- behind schedule The tunnel project has already fallen behind schedule.
- according to schedule At this stage everything is going according to schedule (= as planned).

completed
verb

complete something to finish making or doing something
- to complete a course/project
- to complete a task/mission
- to complete your education/training
- She's just completed a master's degree in Law.
- He has recently completed his first year at Durham University.

- The work should be completed by December.
- She successfully completed the London Marathon in April.

achievable
adjective

(of a goal, status or standard) that can be reached, especially by making an effort for a long time
- Profits of $20m look achievable.
- achievable goals

OPPOSITE unachievable

non-essential
adjective

not completely necessary
- They argue that killing seals for non-essential products cannot be justified.
- We found the travel to be non-essential

determination
noun

[uncountable] the quality that makes you continue trying to do something even when this is difficult
- fierce/grim/dogged determination
- He fought the illness with courage and determination.

- They had survived by sheer determination.
- determination to do something I admire her determination to get it right.

coordination
noun

the act of making parts of something, groups of people, etc. work together in an efficient and organised way
- The aim was to improve the coordination of services.
- coordination between A and B a need for greater coordination between departments
- coordination in something a lack of coordination in conservation policy
- in coordination with somebody/something a pamphlet produced by the government in coordination with (= working together with) the Sports Council
- advice on colour coordination (= choosing colours that look nice together, for example in clothes or furniture)

motivation
noun

[countable, uncountable] the reason why somebody does something or behaves in a particular way
- motivation (behind something) What is the motivation behind this sudden change?

- motivation for (doing) something Most people said that pay was their main motivation for working.
- He's intelligent enough but he lacks motivation.

interaction
noun

interaction (between A and B) | interaction (of A) (with B) the act of communicating with somebody, especially while you work, play or spend time with them
- the interaction between performers and their audience

pacing
verb

[intransitive, transitive] to walk up and down in a small area many times, especially because you are feeling nervous or angry
- + adv./prep. She paced up and down outside the room.
- I paced nervously back and forth across the room.
- pace something Ted paced the floor restlessly.
- [transitive] pace something to set the speed at which something happens or develops
- He paced his game skilfully.
- One runner was selected to pace the race.

recommend
verb

to tell somebody that something is good or useful, or that somebody would be suitable for a particular job, etc.

- recommend somebody/something The hotel's new restaurant comes highly recommended (= a lot of people have praised it).
- Can you recommend a good hotel?
- recommend somebody/something to somebody I recommend the book to all my students.
- recommend somebody/something for something/ somebody She was recommended for the post by a colleague.
- This game is recommended for children aged 12 and above.
- recommend somebody/something as something The guidelines recommend low-fat dairy products as excellent sources of calcium

expensive
adjective

costing a lot of money

- an expensive car/restaurant/holiday
- I can't afford it—it's too expensive.
- Making the wrong decision could prove expensive.

- That dress was an expensive mistake.
- expensive to do Art books are expensive to produce.
- expensive for somebody The new regulations are likely to be very expensive for employers.
- expensive for somebody to do Bonds can be expensive for individuals to invest in.
- it is expensive to do something It's expensive to live in London.
- it is expensive for somebody to do something It is now more expensive for Europeans to visit here.

aspirations
noun

[countable, usually plural, uncountable] a strong desire to have or do something
- I didn't realise you had political aspirations.
- aspiration to do something He has never had any aspiration to earn a lot of money.
- aspiration for something What changes are needed to meet women's aspirations for employment?
- She talked about her hopes and aspirations.
- a political party that fulfils the aspirations of the British people
- an aspiration for personal power
- the country's aspirations to independence
- aspirations towards starting his own business

boundaries

noun

a real or imagined line that marks the limits or edges of something and separates it from other things or places; a dividing line
- After the war the national boundaries were redrawn.
- (British English) county boundaries
- boundary changes/disputes
- The fence marks the boundary between my property and hers.
- Scientists continue to push back the boundaries of human knowledge.
- It is up to the teacher to set the boundary between acceptable and unacceptable behaviour.

promotions

noun

[uncountable, countable] a move to a more important job or rank in a company or an organisation
- The new job is a promotion for him.
- promotion to something Her promotion to Sales Manager took everyone by surprise.
- a job with excellent promotion prospects

University

noun

an institution at the highest level of education where you can study for a degree or do research
- Is there a university in this town?
- Ohio State University
- the University of York
- York University
- at a/the university She studied at the University of Chicago.
- (British English) at university Both their children are at university.
- (British English) He's hoping to go to university next year.

certificates

noun

an official document that may be used to prove that the facts it states are true
- a birth/marriage/death certificate
- certificate of something a certificate of motor insurance
- an official document proving that you have completed a course of study or passed an exam; a qualification obtained after a course of study or an exam
- a Postgraduate Certificate in Education (= a British qualification for teachers)
- certificate of something A certificate of completion will be issued to all who complete the course.

hesitation
noun

[uncountable, countable] the act of being slow to speak or act because you feel uncertain or nervous
- She agreed without the slightest hesitation.
- He spoke fluently and without unnecessary hesitations.

stubborn
adjective

(often disapproving) determined not to change your opinion or attitude
SYNONYM obstinate
- He was too stubborn to admit that he was wrong.
- She can be as stubborn as a mule (= extremely stubborn).
- stubborn pride
- He started out with nothing but raw talent and stubborn determination.

reference/s
noun

[countable, uncountable] a thing you say or write that mentions somebody/something else; the act of mentioning somebody/something
- reference to somebody/something She made no reference to her illness but only to her future plans.

- the President's passing reference to (= brief mention of) the end of the war
- Her book contains many biblical references.
- His testimony included references to memos by the company's financial managers.
- Study their correspondence and you find only three references to George Washington.
- She discreetly avoided any specific reference to religion.
- reference to doing something The book is full of references to growing up in India.
- There are frequent references in the text to the English Civil War.

[countable] a letter written by somebody who knows you, giving information about your character and abilities, especially to a new employer
- I'm sure she'll give you a good reference.
- We will take up references (= contact the people who provided them) after the interview.
- We'll need a reference from your current employer.
- She asked him to provide a reference for her.

physics
noun

the scientific study of matter and energy and the relationships between them, including the study of forces, heat, light, sound, electricity and the structure of atoms

- a degree in physics
- quantum/theoretical physics
- the laws of physics

seriously
adverb

- They are seriously concerned about security.
- You need to think seriously about your next career move.
- He is seriously considering opening a second restaurant.

ambition
noun

something that you want to do or achieve very much
- She had fulfilled her lifelong ambition.
- His burning ambition was to study medicine.
- political/artistic/career ambitions
- At last he had realised his life's ambition.
- He had only one ambition in life.

perspective
noun

a particular attitude towards something; a way of thinking about something
SYNONYM viewpoint

- a global perspective
- A historical perspective may help us understand the issue.
- Recent events seem less serious when put into an international perspective.
- The aim is to offer a fresh perspective.
- from a... perspective Try to see the issue from a different perspective.
- from the perspective of somebody/something a report that looks at the education system from the perspective of deaf people
- perspective on something The exhibition provides us with a unique perspective on her work.

sacrifice

noun

the fact of giving up something important or valuable to you in order to get or do something that seems more important; something that you give up in this way
- The makers of the product assured us that there had been no sacrifice of quality.
- Her parents made sacrifices so that she could have a good education.
- to make the ultimate/supreme sacrifice (= to die for your country, to save a friend, etc.)

identifying
verb

to recognise somebody/something and be able to say who or what they are
- identify somebody/something She was able to identify her attacker.
- Passengers were asked to identify their own suitcases before they were put on the plane.
- identify yourself Many of those arrested refused to identify themselves (= would not say who they were).
- identify somebody/something as somebody/something The bodies were identified as those of two suspected drug dealers.
- identify somebody/something by something two species of waterbirds that can be identified by their distinctive beaks

required
verb

to need something; to depend on somebody/something
- require something These pets require a lot of care and attention.
- Deciphering the code requires an expert.
- This condition requires urgent treatment.

- Do you require anything else? (= in a shop/store, for example)
- These plants absolutely require shade.
- require somebody/something to do something True marriage requires us to show trust and loyalty.
- require that... The situation required that he be present.
- (British English also) The situation required that he should be present.

astrology
noun

the study of the positions of the stars and the movements of the planets in the belief that they influence human affairs
- I read the horoscopes for fun but I don't really believe in astrology.

translate
verb

[transitive, intransitive] to express the meaning of speech or writing in a different language
- translate something into something He translated the letter into English.
- Her books have been translated into 24 languages.
- Can you help me translate this legal jargon into plain English?

- translate something from something This chapter was translated from the French by Oliver Breen.
- translate something from something into something His works have been translated from French into countless languages.
- translate something as something 'Suisse' had been wrongly translated as 'Sweden.'
- translate (something) The novel has been widely translated.
- I don't speak Greek so Dina offered to translate for me.

translate (something) (as something) to understand something in a particular way or give something a particular meaning
SYNONYM interpret
- the various words and gestures that we translate as love

approaching
verb

to come near to somebody/something in distance or time
- We could hear the train approaching.
- Winter is approaching.
- The deadline was fast approaching.
- The rapidly approaching storm could be seen on the horizon.

ironically

adverb

in a way that shows that you really mean the opposite of what you are saying; in a way that expresses irony
- He smiled ironically.

conversation

noun

an informal talk involving a small group of people or only two; the activity of talking in this way
- a phone conversation
- The main topic of conversation was the likely outcome of the election.
- I tried to make conversation (= to speak in order to appear polite).
- conversation with somebody I had a long conversation with her the other day.
- She was engaged in conversation with a colleague.
- (British English) to get into conversation with somebody

discussion

noun

a conversation about somebody/something; the process of discussing somebody/something

- I discovered something interesting during a family discussion.
- We'll continue this discussion some other time.
- discussion with somebody (about somebody/something) We had a discussion with them about the differences between Britain and the US.
- discussion about somebody/something A lively discussion followed about whether he should be allowed to join the club.
- discussion on something The pair held informal discussions on a number of topics.
- discussion around something The exhibition offers opportunities for frank discussions around sensitive issues.

formulate
verb

to create or prepare something carefully, giving particular attention to the details
- formulate something to formulate a policy/theory/plan/proposal
- The compost is specially formulated for pot plants.
- formulate something to do something This new kitchen cleaner is formulated to cut through grease and dirt.

reinforce

verb

reinforce something to make a feeling, an idea, etc. stronger
- The experience reinforced my sense of loss.
- Such jokes tend to reinforce racial stereotypes.
- The climate of political confusion has only reinforced the country's economic decline.
- Success in the talks will reinforce his reputation as an international statesman.

pronounce

verb

pronounce something to make the sound of a word or letter in a particular way
- to pronounce a word/syllable/vowel/consonant
- Very few people can pronounce my name correctly.
- The 'b' in lamb is not pronounced.
- I found it difficult to pronounce the name of the port.

describe

verb

to say what somebody/something is like
- describe somebody/something The next section describes our findings in detail.

- to describe a method/process/situation
- describe somebody/something to somebody Can you describe him to me?
- describe somebody/something for somebody They described for us exactly what happened.
- describe somebody/something as something The man was described as tall and dark, and aged about 20.
- describe yourself as something She describes herself as an artist.
- describe how, what, etc… Describe how you did it.

confrontational
adjective

tending to deal with people in an aggressive way that is likely to cause arguments, rather than discussing things with them
- Why do they take such a confrontational approach towards Europe?
- a confrontational style of management

direct
adjective

going in the straightest line between two places without stopping or changing direction
- the most direct route

- This door allows direct access from the kitchen to the garage.
- saying exactly what you mean in a way that nobody can pretend not to understand
- I asked him a direct question: 'Did you do it?'
- He would not give a direct answer.
- Her response is refreshingly direct.
- Their message is simple and direct: obesity kills.
- You'll have to get used to his direct manner.
- I prefer a more direct approach.

expression
noun

- What's the meaning of the expression 'on cloud nine'?
- She uses a lot of slang expressions that I've never heard before.
- Keep a list of useful words and expressions.
- (informal) He's a pain in the butt, if you'll pardon the expression.

concise
adjective

giving only the information that is necessary and important, using few words
- a concise summary
- he / She gave us clear and concise instructions.

subconsciously

adverb

as a result of feelings that influence your behaviour even though you are not aware of them
- Subconsciously, she was looking for the father she had never known.

impulse

noun

impulse (to do something) a sudden strong wish or need to do something, without stopping to think about the results
- He had a sudden impulse to stand up and sing.
- I resisted the impulse to laugh.
- Her first impulse was to run away.
- on (an) impulse The door was open and on (an) impulse she went inside.
- He tends to act on impulse.

possibility

noun

a thing that may happen or be true; the fact that something might happen or be true, but is not certain
- Bankruptcy is a real possibility if sales don't improve.
- What had seemed impossible now seemed a distinct possibility.

- Reaching the final seems a remote possibility.
- possibility that... There's a strong possibility that it will rain.
- There is now a possibility that she will make a full recovery.

reaction
noun

what you do, say or think as a result of something that has happened
- to provoke/cause/get a reaction
- a positive/negative/adverse reaction
- reaction to something What was his reaction to the news?
- Often our actions are based upon an emotional reaction to what someone has done or said to us.

satisfaction
noun

the good feeling that you have when you have achieved something or when something that you wanted to happen does happen; something that gives you this feeling
- to gain/get/derive satisfaction from something
- a look/smile of satisfaction
- with satisfaction She looked back on her career with great satisfaction.

- He had the satisfaction of seeing his book become a bestseller.
- She didn't want to give him the satisfaction of seeing her cry.
- The company is trying to improve customer satisfaction.

immersed
verb

to become or make somebody completely involved in something
- immerse yourself in something She immersed herself in her work.
- I immediately immersed myself in the task.
- be immersed in something Clare and Phil were immersed in conversation in the corner.

endurance
noun

the ability to continue doing something painful or difficult for a long period of time without giving up
- He showed remarkable endurance throughout his illness.
- This event tests both physical and mental endurance.
- The task was a test of their powers of endurance.

MEANING OF WORDS NOUNS, ADJECTIVES, EXAMPLES

noun – person, place or thing

person – boy, girl, teacher
place – home, school, park
thing – apple, backpack, pencil

pronoun – takes the place of a noun and may replace a name

I, me, we, he, she, they, us, you, it.

verb – describes an action or state of being.

action - run, walk, think, talk
state of being - am, are, was, is

adverb – tells how, when, where or to what extent

how – perfectly
when – yesterday
where – here
extent – completely

adjective - describes a noun or pronoun also says how many, what kind, or which one.

happy, healthy, more, eight, this, that.

article - comes before a noun in a sentence and is a special kind of adjective

A: a boy, a girl, a teacher.
An: an ant, an orange, an airplane
The: the apple, the pencil, the dog

preposition - used with a noun or pronoun to form a phrase

at - at home
from - from work
by - by the lake
with - with us

conjunction - joins words and groups within a sentence

and, except, but, also, either, or

interjection - strong feeling or reaction.

uh-oh! yea! hey! wow! oh-no! oh!

COMMON PUNCTUATION

?   used at the end of a sentence when asking a question

!   used to show excitement or strong emotion at the end of a sentence

" "   used to show speech within a sentence. also used when setting off a phrase, quote or word

-   used to summarise an idea as well as signal a change or break in thought

&   used to represent the word "and"

...   used to indicate a pause or trailing off thought

,   used to indicate a brief pause in a sentence

.   used to indicate the end of a sentence

Letters

BELOW ARE SOME TEMPLATE LETTERS I HOPE YOU CAN FIND USEFUL

your address

date

their address

Dear Sir/Madam
(or person you wish to talk to, e.g. Dear R SMITH)

I wish to raise an issue with your (product, service) which sadly, was not up to standard.

I would like to discuss the matter further to resolve the issue. Please could you be kind enough to call me or contact me on

phone number
email
or at the above address

Yours faithfully,
your name

"faithfully" is if you don't know the person you are writing to or not had contact with them before, i.e. Dear Sir/Madam. Yours sincerely can be used should you know the person.

EXAMPLE OF A COMPLAINT LETTER

your address

date

their address

Dear Sir / Madam
(or person you wish to talk to, e.g. Dear R SMITH)

I wish to thank you for your (product, service). It was really good so I would like to thank you very much.

I would like to discuss how to leave good feedback on this. Please could you be kind enough to call me or contact me on

phone number
email

or at the above address

Yours faithfully,
your name

EXAMPLE OF A COMPLIMENT LETTER
OR LETTER OF THANKS

your address

date

their address

Dear Sir / Madam
(or person you wish to talk to, e.g. Dear R SMITH)

I wish to ask for you help regarding your (product , services)

I would like to discuss in more detail. So, please could you be kind enough to call me or contact me on

phone number
email

or at the above address

Yours faithfully,
your name

EXAMPLE OF AN ASKING FOR ADVICE OR HELP LETTER

your address

date

their address

Dear Sir / Madam
(or person you wish to talk to, e.g. Dear R SMITH)

In response to your advertisement on ....

Thank you for taking the time to read my CV. I believe that I could fit this job well and be a productive member of your team. or company.

(delete either team or company depending on role applied for)

Should you wish to discuss my enclosed CV in any more detail then please feel free to call me or contact me back on

phone number
email

yours faithfully
your name

ACKNOWLEDGEMENTS

A thank you to my lovely lady who supported me while writing this little book.

So… Now… A thank you to my mother who helps me even now…

To my father for his wise ear and calming words of support.

To my younger brother who I am just so proud of.

To my elder bother who has the biggest heart and one of the kindness men I know and respect for it.

To my grandfather and grandmother while you both are sadly no longer with me and you will never get to read it, I have heard you both in my thoughts and in my heart, Thank you always for your guidance.

Words and their meaning

All gathered from the Oxford Advanced Learner's Dictionary.
https://www.oxfordlearnersdictionaries.com/definition/english/

Warner Bros. Studio Tour London

The Making of Harry Potter design department – 5 Images courtesy and a brilliant tour.

BV - #0028 - 261121 - C6 - 234/153/12 [14] - CB - 9781913012595 - Matt Lamination